D1133121

MUST WE HIDE?

MUST WE HIDE?

R. E. LAPP

ADDISON-WESLEY PRESS, INC.

CAMBRIDGE 42, MASS.

1949

Preface

This book is the work of more than one person. I have had the very valuable criticisms of many officers and officials in the National Military Establishment, the Public Health Service, the Atomic Energy Commission, and the National Security Resources Board. These men see the dangers we face, the need for public awareness of them, and the long arduous trek we must make towards the goal of national security. If I have succeeded in correctly translating the thoughts of these men, perhaps, in small measure, I have repaid the debt I owe them.

R. E. Lapp

Washington, D.C.
February 1949

Preface

Washington, D.C.
February 1946

Contents

INTRODUCTION

Today the American people remain in ignorance of many facts about atomic bombing. Eight atomic bombs have been exploded by the United States, but the whole truth about atomic weapons has not been told. The real facts are simple and can be told in simple language. Furthermore, they *can* be told. They are not top secret, secret, or even restricted.

Ever since the day when President Truman announced to a wholly unprepared world that an atomic bomb had been exploded over Hiroshima, the facts about atomic weapons have been hidden in a mumbo-jumbo of half-truths, fiction, and fantasy. Correspondents, armed with a few facts about the atom, soon overcame an initial shyness of the subject and poured forth torrents of words.

Then came Bikini and the world was made conscious of radioactivity. There were 42,000 people at Bikini but only a very few understood what happened there. In the opinion of the author, the real story of Bikini and radioactivity has never been told. The true story, which we shall attempt to tell, is not the sensational one which some have painted. We shall describe the Bikini bomb bursts in detail and we shall try to interpret them realistically, not hysterically.

Three atomic bombs were exploded at the lonely atoll of Eniwetok, not far from Bikini. Veiled in secrecy, these bomb tests, so remote from our mainland, have added to the mysticism of atomic weaponry. Are the present model A-bombs so powerful that they must be detonated in the vastness of the Pacific? After all, the first bomb was tested within the United States at Alamogordo, New Mexico. Just what are the facts? Where will these facts be found?

For the most part, the facts are already published. To be sure, they are not all in one place, otherwise this book would not be necessary. But the data are available. In writing this book, I have tried not only to report the facts in an unemotional manner, but have also attempted to draw logical conclusions from them. The use of secret information has been scrupulously avoided. It is not necessary to have secret data in order to understand the facts about atomic bombs and radioactivity. The average citizen may read this book with the uneasy feeling that there are many secrets which are being kept from him and which he should know. We wish to assure him that such is not the case. The fact that I have complied with all security regulations in no way interfered with the writing of this book. Where opinions are expressed, they are not necessarily those of the National Military Establishment.

Chapter 1
ATOMIC ATTACK

"War is an act of force and to the application of that force there is no limit."

—KARL VON CLAUSEWITZ

The problem of atomic defense is a great one, but it is not *hopelessly* great. Defenses against the bomb *are* possible. There is, and there will be, no complete defense against the bomb, but there are a number of measures which will be effective. Some must be undertaken now; others must be carefully planned for a later date. All will be difficult undertakings, requiring both patience and courage on the part of the people.

We must not take a defeatist attitude toward the bomb. *We must not hide* from the facts. The issues must be faced squarely and must be met with ingenuity and perseverance. We must resolutely face the future with the conviction that an informed America will be an unconquerable nation. David Lilienthal, Chairman of the Atomic Energy Commission, has said, ". . . the people must be informed." But today the American people are not informed. Where, for example, can one find

1

authoritative answers to such questions as: Will there be bombs
powerful enough to wipe out a whole state? Would a bomb
exploded in Lake Michigan send a lethal rain of radioactivity
over all Chicago? Would the explosion of 100 bombs so con-
taminate the world that life would be impossible?

The people of this nation must be told the truth. For only if
the real implications of the atomic bomb are known and understood can we hope to live sanely in the Atomic Age. If this new
weapon is brought into proper perspective, the people will be
able to live with it. The nation must find its guidance and inspiration in the sentiments of its citizens-at-large. We believe
that once the people are informed, they will rise to the challenge of our present dilemma. *We have faith that the people of
this country will survive the atomic bomb.*

                    *   *   *

The atomic bomb entered the history books too soon. Had
it waited for its debut until the 21st century, then, perhaps, it
would have been less of a problem. After all, we are scarcely
advanced into more than the early adolescence of the Air Age.
We are only beginning to extend mutual understanding and
friendship on a personal basis beyond territorial borders.

But the bomb did not wait. To the Americans its advent was
President Truman's electrifying announcement on August 6th,
1945. To the Japanese, awareness had already come as a flash
of blinding light over the city of Hiroshima. But for some
scientists, working on the now famous Manhattan Project, the
announcement was a denouement. For four long years they had
quietly worked in their laboratories. As the day drew near
when the bomb became a probability rather than a possibility,
some atomic scientists paused and thought, "What have we
done?" Up to that time, we thought we were racing against
Germany to develop the bomb. We know now that German
progress in atomic energy was negligible. The Germans were
not even on the right track. When Germany was eliminated

from the war, the incentive was no longer a competitive one; it became a case of saving lives that might otherwise be lost in an invasion of the Japanese home island. So the bomb was used. It is good that the atomic bomb came out into the open. *Had it not been used, free discussion today might not be possible.*

ONE WORLD OR NONE?

At first it seemed very strange for scientists to see the words ATOMIC BOMB, PLUTONIUM, FISSION—all out in the open, in newspapers, on the radio, and in public discussion. After learning to guard every word spoken in public prior to August 6th, scientists suddenly became vocal. Thrust into the limelight, the more eloquent discoursed at length on the atom and on world affairs. They met in small groups, with the best of intentions, and soon came forth with the pronouncement that there was no defense against the A-bomb and that soon other countries would have the bomb. They said there must be One World or None. Then came the sad disillusionment of the postwar era. One world was sharply divided in two. Russia and the United States, wartime allies in the Battle of Europe, strongly disagreed on many questions. It was neither peace nor war.

One World or None! . . . this was a dictum in black and white, unrelieved by any tone of gray. If it is not to be ONE WORLD will it be NONE? Is it only a matter of time before an atomic war breaks out? If so, how soon may this occur? Will it be a lightning war—a superblitz against which there is no defense? Is there a possibility that atomic weapons will not be used? Let us examine some of these questions, beginning with the last one.

AN OUTLAWED WEAPON?

An outlawed weapon has been described as "one which won't be used until necessary." *The history of military weapons indicates that no specific weapon of great utility has ever been really outlawed.* When an aggressor has refrained from using a vicious and despised instrument of warfare, it has usually been because he had assessed its overall usefulness and found it wanting. Gas warfare was introduced on a small scale in World War I and then "outlawed" for use in future wars. In World War II the combatants produced large quantities of lethal gases. They were not used, however, because of the fear of retaliation and because other weapons were proved more effective. In the war in the Pacific we carefully refrained from using gas, yet we employed flamethrowers and anti-personnel incendiaries with abandon. Surely no one would claim that the latter type of warfare is more humane!

Almost every new weapon causes the victimized country to cry out that it is inhumane. Thus it is hoped that the user will feel the weight of popular condemnation and become conscious of guilt. The reader will recall that the British reviled "the dirty Hun" for dropping bombs on London during the first World War, and that the term "baby killers" was freely used. For the fighter pilots who took to the sky to intercept the bomb-carrying Zeppelins and planes, the British expressed lavish praise and the word "ace" was born. In the last war we thought of fighter pilots as heroic figures and somewhat less loudly acclaimed the prowess of the men who flew bombers over enemy cities.

It is not surprising to find that a sense of guilt attached to the use of the atomic bomb, but it is curious that it was the *user* who *voluntarily* assumed the mantle of guilt. Dr. Oppenheimer expressed this sentiment when he said, "In some sort of crude sense which no vulgarity, no humor, no overstatement can quite extinguish, the physicists have known sin and this is a knowledge which they cannot lose."

While some may still debate the issue as to whether atomic bombs will be used in future war, it seems that even church authorities accept their use as inevitable. An Associated Press dispatch from London states that the Church of England

Assembly approved the use of the atomic bomb as a "defensive necessity" against an aggressor. Dr. Cyril F. Garbett, Archbishop of York, said, "The bomb would almost certainly be used if another war broke out."

War today is *total* war, which means that *everyone* is involved . . . the man who makes the gun no less than the man who fires it. In such a war, to which World War II was a close approach for some nations, there are no rules of good conduct. War is a fight to the death. Etiquette and rules of procedure are mockery. Every weapon which can conceivably contribute to the effective prosecution of the war will be used. Atomic weapons most certainly fall within this category and their use is a foregone conclusion.

AN ABSOLUTE WEAPON?

Since the beginning of recorded history man has been engaged in an almost never-ending series of conflicts. Indeed, wars and the preparation for wars have consumed so much of time that it is difficult to recognize years of true peace.

Each war has seen the art of warfare carried one step further. Each war has witnessed the introduction of new weapons. With each new weapon there was often a momentary upset of the age-old equilibrium between the power of offense and defense . . . but no weapon has ever been found to be "absolute" in the sense that its mere possession guaranteed victory. In general, development of the offense was given priority over defense on the basis of the reasoning that the best defense was a good offense. Much ridicule has often attached to those who sought to be impregnable behind massive fortifications such as the Maginot Line. However, in the battle for supremacy no offensive weapons ever achieved complete superiority for any length of time. Very often the desire to test out innovations on a small scale in actual combat prior to an all-out production effort gave the enemy a chance to recover from its initial use and to develop countermeasures. Sometimes the use of newly

introduced weapons backfired. Such was the case with gas warfare, first introduced by the Germans in World War I and
turned against them in a more effective manner by the British.

When organized warfare was still in its infancy, man conducted his offensive operations in a very personal manner. He
simply slugged it out with his foe in person-to-person combat.
The victor was he who excelled in sheer numbers, in agility, or
in better body armor and weapons. Later on, as man became
more adept in the ways of combat, he took to the strategy of
hitting his enemy from a safe distance, where he need not risk
his own neck. To do this he used such devices as the javelin
and the bow and arrow. Then he devised new weapons like the
catapult, which required a team of men for its operation. Gradually the techniques of war evolved into more and more impersonal means of delivering destruction to an enemy, and at a
greater and greater distance from him.

At the same time, men sought to increase the specific power
of the weapons they delivered. Gunpowder, a Chinese invention, was adapted for use in rifles, cannon, and explosive bombs.
The development of the high-explosive bomb seemed to be the
ultimate in an offensive weapon. First we heard of one-ton
bombs, then blockbusters, and finally the 11-ton "Grand Slam."
The combination of heavy bombs and long-range bombers led
many to make dire predictions before the last war. But, as we
shall see later from a review of the bombing of Germany and
Japan, these men were overenthusiastic. Air power did not live
up to the predictions of its potency. Today we are told that
guided missiles and atomic bombs are the ultimate in weapon
development. War, we are told, will not be a long drawn out af-
fair; rather, it will be of short duration.

THE SUPERBLITZ

Hitler introduced the word "blitzkrieg," or lightning war, to
the world. Among the many terms currently in vogue, the name
"superblitz" is most expressive. It conjures up notions of a one-

week, a one-day, or a one-hour war. A war characterized by the descent of ocean-spanning guided missiles carrying atomic warheads; a war that ends almost as soon as it begins; above all, a war in which victory goes to the aggressor. In such a war, the element of surprise is of utmost importance. One pictures the sudden vanishing of our cities if we are attacked. Some imagine that radioactive gases will be used to kill off vast numbers of our populace.

The only thing wrong with the idea of a superblitz is that there is no way to wage one. First of all, sizeable numbers of suitable atomic warheads must be produced, then a guided missile capable of spanning large distances and accurately descending at the prescribed time and place must be developed and produced. Furthermore, it must be determined precisely what targets should be hit and what will be accomplished by hitting them.

Today we do not have transoceanic missiles and even if we had they would be useless unless they could be accurately guided to their targets. It will be a long time before we attain the degree of perfection implied in the words "push-button warfare." One has a mental picture of wars being fought by neat little men in trim uniforms sitting before long rows of instrument panels, sending huge rockets zooming off to a foreign land. A tidy sort of war—impersonal and even fastidious!

Some people have been deluded into thinking that the superblitz age is here. At the end of the last war, the Germans had sent hundreds of V–2 rockets high across the Channel to land on London. All this seemed ominous. All one had to do was to pick up where the Germans had left off, revamp the V–2, extend its range a few thousand miles, and arm it with an atomic warhead. Then we could have intercontinental warfare. Many scientists reasoned thus and the public, awed by the incredibility of the atomic development, accepted the concept of a long-range rocket warfare without a murmur.

However, the step from the V–2 to a transoceanic missile is

a very large one. The development of such a missile will be much more of a job than even the developing of the atomic bomb. And if it should bear fruit, it may well be that the cost per missile will be too serious a drain upon our resources. In an undertaking of this kind, much of which may remain in a research stage for a long time, it is difficult to predict how soon the development will culminate but it seems safe to say that intercontinental missiles are many years in the future.

SPACE IS OUR ALLY

If we are not to have transoceanic missiles for many years, we must still consider the delivery of atomic bombs by long-range bombers. In the past, the great oceans bordering our continent have given us a real measure of security against foreign aggression. It might seem that the advent of the high-speed, long-range bomber has materially altered the sense of this security. Has not the close coincidence of the Atomic Age with the Air Age enormously enhanced the striking power of the latter? Actually, the Air Age is still too young to provide means of delivering atomic bombs over 5,000 miles at sonic speeds. It will probably be many years before any country can boast of truly long-range, high-speed aircraft capable of decisive intercontinental warfare. We would make a serious mistake, however, if we assumed that only a very high speed bomber would get through to its target. The defense can not furnish opposition unless it detects the presence of the invader in time to activate its forces. With radar networks stretched over vast distances and fighter bases spread thin, the problem of intercepting enemy bombers, even slow ones, is extremely difficult. Some bombers will always get through and the faster they travel, the more will reach their targets. But air attack alone will not win a war even with atomic bombs. Thus space beyond our borders still isolates us—not perfectly but to a significant degree.

Within our borders, too, we have plenty of space. One of the most decisive things which we as a country can do to reduce our vulnerability to atomic attack is to use this space effectively. This space is really our ally. Germany has far less space than we, but it was able to use it to advantage in the dispersal of industry. Unfortunately for Hitler, dispersal was delayed too long to be truly effective. In this country we must not be blind to the lessons of the last war even if they are learned from nonatomic weapons.

Our cities today are excellent targets for an aggressor. Ten years from now they will be even better targets unless we do something about them very soon. We cannot assume that an invading force of bombers can be wholly intercepted; some will get through despite our best efforts. We must be capable of absorbing the punishment these inflict and to do so we must make our targets as unattractive and as invulnerable as possible. Thus we will lessen the feasibility of an aggressor's success in an atomic attack. At the same time we will be molding our cities into places better adapted for living and better suited to modern means of local transportation. Most of our cities already reflect the fact that they are better suited to the horse and buggy than to the automobile. This reconstruction of our cities—call it decentralization, or advanced city planning, or dispersion—will be costly. However, we spend billions each year for an Army, a Navy, and an Air Force . . . and these agencies are essentially pure consumers. They do not directly enhance our life in material ways. An airplane is very soon outmoded and has no value except for scrap; the expenditure of several billion dollars per year to encourage construction of less vulnerable cities and industries would be of long-term value. Furthermore, the dispersion of our cities and the formation of smaller city units will greatly enhance the happiness of the average city dweller.

Dispersal of vital facilities is not only possible but feasible. Even atomic bombs meet their master in the invincibility of space. Even improved atomic bombs produce serious damage over only a limited area. We can assure ourselves a measure of security by planning well laid out cities in which the number of people per square mile, unlike Manhattan or Hiroshima, is relatively low. Furthermore, we can provide some measure of protection to existing facilities by constructing shelters. If a city is alerted for an atomic attack and has suitable shelters, it can reduce the death toll from a bomb burst from 100,000, which might be expected with no protection, to less than 10,000. Shelters would not be prohibitively expensive and could be built easily.

THE INTERIM PERIOD

It is encouraging to know that shelters against A-bombs can be made effective but for the larger and more difficult task of remolding the pattern of our cities, the layman is justified in asking, "Is there time to do this?" Often the question is paraphrased, "When will an enemy have the A-bomb?" *These two questions are not the same.* In fact, the question as to when an enemy will have the bomb is irrelevant. More important than to know when an enemy has produced its first atomic bomb is to know *how many bombs per year* will be produced. It seems reasonable to assume that other nations will not develop bombs until 1952, seven years after our first atomic test. No one knows the exact date. We feel that we are being rather conservative in choosing 1952, for there are a number of competent authorities who say that it will take much longer for others to develop the bomb.

Before an enemy can accumulate a respectable stock pile of atomic bombs, it will take at least as many years as it is taking for the development of its first one. Thus, according to our estimate, it will be about 1960 before others can conceivably have a sizable supply of A-bombs. But this is only one part of the story. *To have the bombs is not enough.* They must be delivered to their targets.

There is thus an interim period of over ten years during which we must continue to explore every possible approach to the

problem of world peace. However, we must never relax our efforts to maintain pre-eminence in the field of atomic weapons.
To do so would be to invite disaster. For us it will be the period
of the armed truce. We hope it is not the lull before the storm.
There is yet time to consider how order may be brought into
the relations between the major powers. During this interim
period we must also use the time to analyze carefully the effectiveness of our National Military Establishment. Objective
thinking must be done in terms of *national security* and not in
terms of an Army, a Navy, or an Air Force—or what each of
these Departments chooses to define as its mission.

It is obvious that the layman can not hope to understand in
detail what has come from the laboratories. The mere mention
of the word "radioactivity" has a numbing effect. It is placed in
the same category as smallpox or rabies. But for these miscon-
ceptions the people themselves are not to blame. It is quite possible for the average man to understand the dangers of radioactivity. Radioactivity is just one more of the hazards of con-
temporary living and must be viewed as such. The layman does
not need to study nuclear physics or medicine to understand
this aspect of atomic weapons.

Chapter 2
ATOMIC BOMB CASUALTIES

"The evil that men do lives after them . . ."
—SHAKESPEARE

As the disaster-dazed survivors of Hiroshima slowly returned to a consciousness of their surroundings, they were not aware that they had been subjected to a new and unusual type of weapon. Many indeed were temporary survivors only who would later succumb to the delayed effects of penetrating radiation already absorbed. Many hours or even days would elapse before some realized that something new had been added to the usual bomb effects of blast and fire. Unusual signs were the large area destroyed by a small number of planes, the huge number of fires, and the large number of casualties showing burns of a different type from those seen after previous bombing raids. Later, as the symptoms of radiation sickness developed, all recognized that they had been targets for an entirely new type of weapon.

RADIATION DEATHS

It is scarcely possible to obtain an accurate estimate of the proportions of casualties due separately to blast, fire, and radiation. Who can establish the cause of death for a person near ground zero (the point on the ground directly under the point of detonation) who had received a many-times lethal dose of penetrating radiation accompanied by a searing wave of thermal radiation, who was then subjected to an extremely high-pressure blast wave and all manner of flying missiles torn from shattered buildings, and who was finally trapped by a multitude of secondary fires? An estimate of the various causes of death in the Japanese blasts might be

Flash burns	25 percent
Radiation injury	15 percent
Blast and other	60 percent

but these are not accurate, scientifically determined figures.

The "overhitting" described is characteristic of an atomic bomb detonation. In an air burst bomb the blast pressures over a considerable area are greater than are required to destroy most buildings and all human life. Similarly the doses of penetrating radiation greatly exceed lethal values out to a considerable distance from ground zero. The term "considerable" is used deliberately; to attempt to give accurate values would be misleading. Destructive radii will depend on many factors, such as topography of the area, the height of detonation, and the effectiveness of the weapon. At Hiroshima persons in the open at 4,000 feet from ground zero received lethal doses of radiation.

All of the survivors of the Japanese blasts agreed that each explosion was heralded by a blinding flash of light, described as equal to many suns, which seemed so close that each felt that the bomb had exploded directly over him. Travelling along with this visible light, felt but unseen by the survivors, was an intense flash of thermal radiation. The highly penetrating gamma rays, arriving simultaneously with the other radiations, were unnoticed by those who absorbed them. By the time the flash was recognized the other radiations had been absorbed and taking shelter was of no avail.

Some of the survivors showed evidences of severe burns within a few minutes after the detonation. Other burns, less severe, developed within a few hours. Because of the short duration of the flash of thermal radiation even thin clothing afforded some protection. More radiation was reflected from light colored cloth than from darker materials and many curious burn patterns resulted. The flash burns healed uneventfully unless infection set in. The only abnormality appeared to be in the abnormally large amount of keloid, or scar tissue, and this may be a racial characteristic of the Japanese. Japanese doctors state that their race does not have a tendency toward the formation of heavy keloids but unusually heavy scars have been observed after the removal of skin for plastic surgery. Medical facilities were almost nonexistent after both of the Japanese blasts and it is probable that the heavy keloid formations resulted chiefly from inadequate treatment.

Many of the burns, either from the initial flash or from secondary fires, were horribly disfiguring, and the formation of the heavy keloids emphasized the grotesque appearances. But the much publicized burns from an atomic blast are no worse than those resulting from other forms of modern weapons. Fig. 2–1 (p. 88) shows a survivor of the Tokyo incendiary raids and Fig. 2–2 (p. 89) a survivor of the Nagasaki atomic bomb. Both men show heavy keloid formation with no significant differences in the severity of the injuries. Severe burns from any cause are disfiguring and incapacitating.

RADIATION SICKNESS

Radiation sickness produces symptoms and injuries which may vary from one individual to another and which depend upon the dose received. The symptoms observed at Hiroshima and Nagasaki, not at all understood by the survivors, are quite familiar to all radiologists. A description of the biological effects of large doses of radiation is not pleasant. They are discussed here with no thought of creating fear or revulsion but in the hope that a thorough understanding of radiation hazards will result in a more realistic acceptance of the weapon. A complete description of the injuries inflicted by almost any modern weapon would be equally gruesome.

Some persons who received massive doses of radiation, as at one-half mile from ground zero, appeared to be uninjured but collapsed and died within a few hours. Some of these deaths may have been due to internal injuries produced by the blast but an atomic blast does not have the extreme shocking power of an ordinary high explosive and most of these early deaths must be ascribed to radiation. In their passage through the body the radiations will react with the atoms and molecules with sufficient force to disrupt chemical bonds and produce new molecular configurations. The economy of the body, normally maintained in a very delicate balance, is upset at a thousand and one places and the person rapidly succumbs.

People who were at greater distances, or who were partially shielded, absorbed smaller amounts of radiation. In these cases the first signs of radiation injury appeared on the first or the second day. Usual symptoms were nausea and vomiting accompanied by a loss of appetite, headache, bloody diarrhea, fever, malaise, and extreme lassitude. The severity of the symptoms varied with the dose received and usually decreased after a few days. It is difficult to be sure that all of these cases were the result of radiation injury, for similar symptoms may appear after great emotional stress or shock.

In the next phase of the sickness, however, the distinction is clear. The first sign of this phase is the severe loss of hair which usually starts abruptly about two weeks after the injury and may continue to complete baldness that may be temporary or permanent (Fig. 2–3, p. 90). Bloody diarrhea, high fever, and prostration usually return during this period. At about one month signs of injury to the blood and the blood-forming organs become evident. Bleeding gums and the appearance of many small hemorrhagic spots under the skin are the outward signs. Laboratory examinations will reveal a severe destruction of the blood cells and the bone marrow that produces them. In the severe cases the white blood cell count will range from a few hundred to one thousand, the normal value being about seven thousand. Since the white blood cells are the active agents in combating infections, the patients will have a very low resistance. Small, normally insignificant wounds may be slow in healing or may develop into large infected areas. The red blood cells are more resistant to radiation than the whites but they will suffer some destruction and signs of anemia are usually present.

The prognosis in these cases is variable and depends upon the severity of the symptoms, with recovery doubtful if the white count falls below one thousand. In the milder cases the symptoms gradually disappear and the patient recovers, although excessive fatigue may be present for many months.

THE SURVIVORS

The array of injuries described seems impressive enough but the story is not yet complete. Both males and females may be made either temporarily or permanently sterile. Even if fertility returns, the reproductive cells have probably suffered permanent damage and mutations or the transmittal of abnormal heredity are possible. This is one of the most publicized effects of radiation injury and it is important to see it in proper perspective.

The basic element of living matter, the cell, exists in many different specific forms, such as brain cells, kidney cells, or liver cells. The nucleus of each cell contains a set of chromosomes, threadlike structures which carry along their lengths the genes or heredity determining components. When most cells divide, the chromosome structure is exactly duplicated and each new cell will have exactly the same characteristics as the original. In sperm or egg cells, however, only half of the original number of chromosomes is passed on and the original number will only be regained when fertilization occurs and an egg and a sperm combine to form the first cell of the offspring. Each gene determines a specific bodily characteristic and if the structure of a gene is altered, as it can be by radiation, the result is a mutation or an altered heredity in the offspring.

The practical effects of mutations are apt to be greatly exaggerated. It is easy to conjure up a picture of a world populated largely by monsters resulting from radiation-induced mutations. There is no doubt that the possibility of producing an abnormal child exists, but *the chance for this is exceedingly small and the offspring will not be monsters.* Living creatures on this earth are and have always been exposed to naturally occurring radiation and there have always been some abnormal births.

A small percentage of the genetic changes will be *dominant* and will be evident in the first generation after that in which the change occurred. Many of the changes will be *lethal,* which means that the embryo will die soon after its conception. Other genetic changes will be *recessive* and will not appear in succeeding generations until there is a mating of two identical recessives. Obviously, the chance of such a mating is very small even though large numbers of people have been exposed. The genetic effects in Japan are so small that no freaks and monsters have been observed. Rather, teams of scientists are making careful, detailed searches for radiation-induced mutations.

Some of the concern about the genetic effects of radiation arises from a failure to distinguish between libido, impotence, and sterility. In at least one audience genuinely concerned with the insidious effects of radiation, there was general relief when the speaker pointed out that even large doses of radiation have little effect on libido and potency!

Plants with abnormal coloring and leaves have been observed growing in the bombed areas and these may be the results of mutations produced by the radiation. All of the mutants may not be less useful or desirable than the parents. Radiation is being used extensively in a search for more productive and hardy varieties of plants and some of the results are encouraging.

One of the insidious effects of radiation is the delayed production of cancer. Usually cancer does not appear for ten or twenty years after the radiation has been received but there is little data on its production in man by a single massive dose. Most of the radiation cancers have been observed in radiologists who have been rather regularly exposed to the radiations from x-ray tubes or radium. The production of cancer appears to be a chance phenomenon in which the chance increases with the dose received. It is interesting to speculate on the mechanism by which radiation produces cancer yet can be used to cure it. One of the common types of radiation cancer is leukemia, in which enormous numbers of white blood cells are produced. This is in sharp contrast to the early effects, where a low white count is one of the most consistent findings.

The list of injuries resulting from the absorption of radiation is an appalling one and might seem to call for an immediate outlawing of radioactive weapons. Actually all modern war puts a severe strain on the participants and who can say that the victim of an atomic attack suffers more than the victim of a flamethrower or a person who has broken down mentally under the stress of combat? Much of the revulsion against the use of atomic weapons arises because the very newness makes it seem more horrible. A careful cataloguing of the injuries resulting from the use of the automobile would also be impressive but any proposal to outlaw the automobile would be considered ridiculous.

THE TOLL

Total casualty figures for the two Japanese bursts are somewhat uncertain because of the lack of accurate census figures before the blasts and because of the confusion that existed afterwards. Estimates indicate that there were about 245,000 people in Hiroshima at the time of the attack. Of these over

71,000 were killed and about 68,000 were injured. Because of the small number of planes sighted, the people paid little attention and few bothered to take shelter. This fact contributed to the large number of casualties. At Nagasaki *people in underground shelters suffered little injury* even when the shelters were near ground zero.

The almost complete disruption of relief facilities helped to raise the death toll. In Hiroshima over ninety percent of the doctors were casualties and only three out of forty-five hospitals were useable. Thousands of breaks in the water pipes resulted in a complete loss of pressure, nearly half of the sewage pumping systems were ruined, and the rest were not operated. It is remarkable that with this almost complete breakdown in sanitary facilities there was no serious epidemic. Under present conditions cities in the United States would fare no better if subjected to atomic attack. In many of our cities important medical facilities are located close to the points of probable attack and would suffer severe damage. Our public utilities and sanitation facilities are about as vulnerable as those in Japan.

At Nagasaki, as at Hiroshima, the appearance of only a few planes did not alert the city and only a few hundred people were in the underground shelters at the time of the blast. Here the force of the bomb was confined by hills to one section of the city and as a result the death toll was slightly over 40,000, with about the same number injured. Although numerous fires broke out, the fire storm of Hiroshima was not repeated. Water pressure could not be maintained and other utilities were severely damaged. As at Hiroshima, most of the medical facilities were wiped out. Over eighty percent of the hospital beds were within 1,000 yards of ground zero and these were completely demolished. Seventy percent of the students at the Nagasaki Medical College were killed and many others were injured. The absence of an epidemic was again striking.

Undoubtedly many lives could have been saved if large scale medical services had been available soon after the explosions.

Most of those that could have been saved would have been
burn and blast injury cases. Medical science had little to offer
for severe radiation injury cases and deaths from this cause
would probably have been little affected if adequate medical
facilities had been available. What the future holds for this
type of casualty can not be predicted. Undoubtedly many borderline cases can be saved with our present knowledge. Whole
blood can be administered until the injured tissues regenerate.
Penicillin and other drugs are valuable in controlling infection.
Some control of internal bleeding may be achieved. Extensive
research programs are underway in an attempt to determine the
mechanism by which radiation kills and injures and future developments may produce more useful treatments.

STUDY GROUPS

Soon after the announcement by President Truman that the
Hiroshima bomb had derived its energy from nuclear fission
Japanese scientists moved into the area and carried out extensive studies. The physicists soon confirmed the fact that a
considerable amount of radioactivity had been produced in the
explosion and they were able to measure the extent of the remaining contamination. The physicians recognized the symptoms of radiation sickness in many of the survivors, realizing
however that little could be done to aid in the repair of the
damage done to the body cells.

Teams of American and British investigators entered the
stricken areas as soon as possible and carried out extensive
studies on all phases of the bomb action. The U. S. Strategic
Bombing Survey had been making an exhaustive study of the
effects of bombing on Germany and moved into Japan in
October, 1945.

Much of the data presented here are taken from the reports
of this survey. The Strategic Bombing Survey was completed in
December, 1945. Late in 1946 President Truman directed the
National Research Council to inaugurate a long-term study of

the biological effects of the explosions. The Atomic Bomb Casualty Commission was formed as a result of this directive. Headquarters were established near the bombed areas and intensive studies initiated. Because of the long delayed effects of penetrating radiations, many years will be required to obtain adequate data. Much information has already been accumulated and published but it is too early to draw any general conclusions. Several generations must be studied before the genetic effects can be analyzed and the task of keeping track of the survivors as they move to various locations is a difficult one but with persistence a large amount of valuable data should be obtained.

Whatever the detailed findings of the Commission, it is certain that there will be no large number of genetic abnormalities resulting from even large-scale atomic attacks. Some delayed cancers may result from excessive exposure of individuals to radiation but there is no evidence that these will be transmitted to successive generations. There is no reason to expect a decided change in the normal pattern of human evolution due to the advent of atomic weapons.

Chapter 3
AIR BURST ATOMIC BOMBS

"Lastly, Science unfolded her treasures and her secrets to the desperate demands of men, and placed in their hands agencies and apparatus almost decisive in their character."

— WINSTON CHURCHILL

Before detonation, an atomic bomb is mildly radioactive, emitting alpha particles that can travel only a few inches in air. In a fraction of a second this quiescent material can be transformed by the chain reaction into an incandescent mass of incredible temperature emitting enormous numbers of penetrating gamma rays capable of killing at nearly one mile. This transformation is accompanied by a series of phenomena which combine to produce the greatest man-made spectacle on earth.

THE EXPLOSION

The survivors of the Japanese atomic bombings, who were the closest observers, all agreed on the main features of the explosions. The first sign was a brilliant flash of an intensity beyond description. Seconds later all was chaos as the blast wave destroyed buildings and hurled people and debris over considerable distances. After this phase, the descriptions become vague, uncertain, and contradictory. So great was the shock and confusion that few were able to observe and remember pertinent details. This confusion is not restricted to people subjected to an atomic attack. The phenomena accompanying an air burst are so complex and occur on such a grand scale with such rapidity that even trained observers, carefully briefed and in absolutely safe locations, differ substantially in their accounts of the spectacle. In the main, however, the phenomena are quite well understood both from theory and from photographic records, which do not have the faulty memories of human observers.

During the fraction of a second taken up by the chain reaction, an enormous amount of energy is liberated in a confined space and the bomb and its immediate surroundings are raised to a temperature measured in millions of degrees. Simultaneously vast numbers of neutrons and gamma rays (the penetrating radiations) are released and move outward from the point of origin. The high temperature produces great pressure, which blows the bomb apart and stops the chain reaction. Many people have expressed the fear that the chain reaction might spread to the surrounding air and continue until the earth was completely destroyed. Actually, nuclear chain reactions are practically possible in only a few materials of a certain critical size. When the bomb blows itself apart, the chain reaction in the original material terminates and there is no possibility for air or any other surrounding material to enter into the reaction.

The high temperature and pressure are transmitted to the surrounding air and a luminous, expanding sphere of highly compressed gas is produced. This is the fireball, which sweeps out several hundred feet from the center. Fig. 3–1 (p. 91) is a photograph of a partially developed fireball. As it expands, the fireball drops in temperature to a few thousand degrees at the edge. Because of its temperature, the fireball will radiate heat rays, visible light, and ultraviolet light at high but decreasing intensities as the gas cools. The thermal and visible components from the initial flash and the fireball produce the flash burns and the surface scorching shown in Fig. 3–2 (p. 92). The amount of this radiation is so great that in Japan unprotected skin was burned at two and one-half miles and the heat blast was felt at nearly five miles. Scorched telegraph poles were observed at about two miles.

THE MUSHROOM

At the center the mass of hot gases and bomb residue rises at an initial rate of nearly one hundred miles an hour to form the now familiar mushroom cloud, Fig. 3–3 (p. 93). The high-pressure wave that moves outward is followed by an inward rush of air that restores the central region to normal pressure. As this air rushes in it sweeps along the surface of the ground, picking up tons of soil and carrying it into the cloud. This surface cleansing action tends to remove radioactive materials deposited from the bomb and carries them into the cloud.

The amount of radioactivity carried upward is almost beyond comprehension. It is customary to compare amounts of radiation with the quantity of radium that will produce the same amount of activity. This is a useful comparison because radium has been in common medical use for many years and is familiar to many people. For example, the total supply of purified radium in the United States is less than two pounds. Another comparison is obtained from the fact that a worker with radium should not be permitted to have more than about one-billionth of a pound fixed or stored in his body. Soon after the explosion the total radioactivity in the cloud will be equivalent to that from thousands of tons of radium. The radioactivity decreases with time but during the first few hours any prolonged contact with the cloud would result in fatal doses of radiation. Unmanned drone airplanes can be flown through the cloud within a few minutes of its formation, since the radioactivity does not interfere with the functioning of the engines and controls. After landing, however, the drones may be highly contaminated with radioactive materials and must be approached with caution.

In an air burst a large percentage of the radioactive products is carried up in the cloud and the residual ground contamination is relatively slight. Japanese physicists entered the bombed areas within a few days after the explosions and found the activities to be only a few times the normal amount produced by natural sources. This is about one-millionth of that required for a fatal dose and about one-thousandth of that allowed for workers regularly exposed for long periods of time.

Plant life returned promptly and so abundantly to the bombed areas that many people believed that the radiations had a stimulating effect on plant growth. A more probable explanation is that large quantities of minerals such as potassium and calcium from pulverized buildings increased the productivity of the soil. Rebuilding of the destroyed areas was underway within a few months and there is no reason to believe that the inhabitants will suffer harm from the remaining radioactivity.

FALL-OUT

At the top of its rise the mushroom will reach an altitude of several miles, with a stem extending down to the point of detonation. This cloud consists of condensed moisture, dust particles, bomb fragments, and the radioactive fission products resulting from the nuclear explosion. The fission products are in the form of small particles ranging in size from single atoms to aggregates several thousandths of an inch in diameter. As the cloud moves away from over the point of detonation under the influence of the prevailing winds, the particles will fall toward the earth. The largest will fall most rapidly, smaller ones will take many hours or days to reach the earth, and those of atomic size will behave much like a gas and may remain suspended indefinitely.

Because of this fall-out the cloud will leave a radioactive

trail for many miles. Using sensitive instruments, Japanese physicists were able to determine the fall-out trail from each of the bombs. Even though the total amount of radioactivity in the cloud is large, the fall-out at any one point will not be a menace to health, since only a small fraction is deposited. Late fall-out will be very weak indeed because of the decay of the radioactivity before the particles return to the earth. Cattle fifty miles from the test explosion at Alamogordo were subjected to fall-out which settled on their backs and heads. The hair growing in the presence of the fission products turned white but there are no signs of serious systemic reactions. Fig. 3–4 (p. 94) shows some of these cattle many months after they experienced the fall-out. The white patches of hair are quite evident but otherwise the cattle appear healthy.

The loss of hair color was due primarily to the absorption of beta rays from the fission products. Beta rays are readily absorbed and have a range of only a few feet in air and one inch in body tissue. Consequently they are a health hazard only when they are emitted from materials which have gained entrance into the body or are in close contact with the skin. Prompt bathing will remove most radioactive materials and it is probable that the cattle would have showed no signs of radiation exposure if they had been out in a heavy rain soon after the fall-out.

GAMMA RAYS

Gamma rays, on the other hand, are very penetrating and constitute the hazard from radioactive materials not in direct contact with the body. Gamma rays are pulses of electromagnetic radiation and travel with the velocity of visible light. They have properties identical with x-rays although they are produced in a quite different manner. Most of the gamma rays associated with the bomb explosion have energies greater (and consequently are more penetrating) than the x-rays produced by the usual medical equipment but are comparable to the x-rays from the high voltage installations used for deep cancer therapy.

There are two distinct gamma ray hazards associated with the detonation. The flash of gamma rays that occurs at the instant of detonation is very intense. The intensity decreases with distance and some of the gamma rays are absorbed as they pass through the air but they may still be lethal at 4000 feet.

The second gamma ray hazard comes from the radioactive fission products left from the blast or deposited from the cloud. As we have seen, in an air burst most of the fission products are carried up in the cloud for later deposition over many square miles and many months. Even though the fission product activity decays with time there may be no difficulty in detecting it for several years. *The range between the limits of detection and lethality is wide,* however (about 100,000,000 times), and fission products from an air burst bomb must be regarded as something of a nuisance but a negligible factor in causing death. In the following chapter we shall see that the situation is quite different when the bomb is exploded under water.

THE NEUTRON FLASH

We must now return to consider the neutrons that started and sustained the chain reaction until it was terminated by its own violence. The neutron has been known only since 1932 yet has assumed an all-important place in the production of nuclear reactions. Neutrons are electrically neutral particles that are able to penetrate easily into the nucleus, the heart of the atom. There they are very apt to be captured and consequently a free neutron has a very short life and is not found except during and shortly after it has been forcibly ejected from a nucleus. When a nucleus of Uranium 235 or of Plutonium 239 absorbs a neutron the structure becomes unstable and splits into two roughly equal fragments. This process is known as fission and the fragments are fission products. In the fission process some free neutrons will be ejected and some of these will be absorbed by other nuclei to produce the chain reaction.

As the bomb blows apart the last generation of neutrons born from the previous fissions will be free to move outward and add to the radiation hazard. Some of the neutrons have high velocities but none has the velocity of light. As the neutrons move out from the center, they experience many collisions with atomic nuclei. In some of the collisions the neutrons will be slowed down and in others they will be captured. As neutrons are slowed the chance for capture becomes greater and within a few minutes all will have entered nuclei.

When a neutron is absorbed by a nucleus the latter may become radioactive and emit radiations that add to those from the fission products. Some atoms have a high affinity for neutrons and can be made strongly radioactive. At Bikini much of the soap left on the target vessels was found to be radioactive from neutron-induced activity in the sodium. Some of the bodies found at Hiroshima were very mildly radioactive, which showed that the victim had been exposed to neutrons as well as to gamma rays. The induced radioactivity was so small that there was no health hazard to anyone treating the injured or removing the dead. Neutrons are the only emissions from the explosion that produce induced radioactivity on a practical scale. Gamma rays do not induce radioactivity and shielding materials which have been absorbing large amounts of gamma radiation are completely innocuous when removed from the sources of the rays.

Because of the nature of the neutron, the neutron flash from the bomb does not have the range of the gamma rays. At Hiroshima the neutron flash was probably inconsequential beyond 1,500 feet. There was little neutron-induced radioactivity in the soil near the Japanese bursts and since there are no neutrons associated with the fall-out of fission products the only neutron hazard in an air burst comes from the initial flash.

PROTECTIVE SHELTERS

Protection against the flash of thermal radiation is easily accomplished. Even the lightest clothing worn in Japan afforded some protection and the most flimsy houses offered complete protection except for the areas occupied by windows. Glass is used in windows because it readily transmits visible light and a considerable fraction of the invisible thermal radiations. In Japan many surface burns were observed on house furnishings located opposite windows whereas similar materials in other parts of the same rooms showed no evidence of scorching.

Gamma ray shielding can best be accomplished by the liberal use of lead but this is obviously economically impossible for large shelters designed to protect large numbers of people. Fortunately, other cheaper materials are also quite effective in stopping gamma rays: a three-inch thickness of concrete will absorb about one-half of the incident gamma rays. A given thickness of absorber will remove the same fraction of the incident gamma rays without regard to the total number of gamma

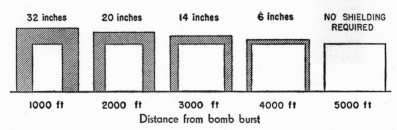

Fig. 3–5 Thicknesses of concrete required for survival.

rays involved. Thus a three-inch slab of concrete will absorb one-half of the gamma rays and will allow one-half to pass through. If a second three-inch slab is placed directly behind the first the second will pass one-half of what it receives or one-fourth of the original. Three three-inch slabs (or one nine-inch slab) will pass one-eighth of the original and so on.

Some of the consequences of this type of absorption are shown in Fig. 3–5. Here are illustrated the thicknesses of concrete walls sufficient to prevent death from radiation at various distances from the burst. The figures given assume that there are no windows which will freely admit radiation and allow it to be scattered in all directions.

Solid earth is not as effective as concrete in stopping gamma rays but a thickness of six feet will reduce even the intensities found near ground zero to safe values. Earth is also a good absorber of neutrons, although more effective materials can be used on a smaller scale. Moist earth is more effective than dry, since there is more hydrogen present to slow down the neutrons so that they can be more readily captured. Ordinary building materials will not be made dangerously radioactive by exposure to a bomb burst.

Chapter 4
BIKINI: TEST BAKER

"The end of the earth will be when some enormous boiler . . . shall explode and blow up our globe. And they (the Americans) are great boilermakers."
—JULES VERNE

Test Able was over. An air burst atomic bomb had been pitted against a target array of naval vessels and had sunk five of them and inflicted damage on many others. Measurements had been made which would show that had the ships been manned many personnel would have perished from the radiation flash even though their ships remained afloat. The slight radioactive contamination left from the air burst bomb did not prevent work on readying the target fleet for the new Test Baker.

The Navy had good reason to conduct the tests at Bikini. The test at Alamogordo showed that the bomb was a weapon of extraordinary power. Hiroshima and Nagasaki proved its effectiveness against centers of population. But what would it do to naval vessels? The modern, highly compartmented fighting ship is an extremely rugged structure designed to take tremendous punishment before losing its fighting efficiency.

Obviously, at least two tests would be necessary. An air burst bomb would subject the topside structures to blast and radiation but comparatively little energy would be transmitted through the water to strike at the underwater portions. Conversely, a bomb exploded in shallow water would produce an intense water shock wave that would act directly on the submerged structures. A deep underwater shot would produce water shock waves of extreme intensity but would probably yield little information of immediate value to the Navy, since the bomb is of doubtful value against a dispersed fleet at sea. Few expressed regret when the deep water burst, Test Charlie, was postponed indefinitely.

The Bikini tests were the most elaborate weapons tests ever conducted. The target ships were anchored in positions carefully chosen to yield the greatest amount of information rather than in the normal disposition of an anchorage. From weather decks to cargo holds they were crammed with all manner of Army and Navy gear. Animals were placed on many of the ships so that the radiation effects on living tissues could be studied and the shielding effects of deck and hull structures determined. Innumerable gages, meters, and gadgets were used to obtain all sorts of scientific information. Some of the best scientific brains in the country were on hand to see that everything was in proper working order and to interpret the readings.

Able day had been rather uneventful. Experience with the three other air burst bombs permitted a rather accurate prediction of the phenomena to be anticipated and when these predictions were fulfilled none of the scientists was particularly surprised. Practically all phases of the Able operation went off as scheduled and preparations for Baker were well under way within a few days after the air burst.

JULY 25, 1946

Tension was high in Bikini lagoon on the night of July 24–25, 1946 and many people throughout the world were disturbed by the pending event. For the first time an atomic bomb was to be exploded at a moderate depth under water. Crack phenomenologists had been working on predictions so that all observers could be stationed in absolutely safe locations yet sufficiently close to permit useful observations of events. The job of transferring data from air bursts to a shallow water burst was not an easy one and there were places where accurate figures had to be replaced by educated guesses.

There was general agreement among the experts on the main phenomena to be expected—only the magnitude of some effects was uncertain. Before the test there were a great variety of predictions originating from all parts of the world. Some expected a gigantic tidal wave that would engulf the active fleet and sweep over the ocean, wreaking havoc over enormous distances. Others predicted that a deep fissure would be riven in the ocean floor, permitting the ocean waters to come in contact with the molten center of the earth with cataclysmic results. Still others felt that the chain reaction in the bomb might spread to the surrounding water and lead to the formation of a new incandescent star.

Most of these dire predictions resulted from a failure to consider carefully the action and power of the bomb. To be sure, a blast that is equivalent to that of 20,000 tons of high explosive is a potent force but how pitifully small when compared with the forces of nature! The total energy in the San Francisco earthquake has been estimated as 100,000 times that released in the atomic bomb. Consider the havoc wrought by a hurricane, where the damage approaches the maximum produced by the bomb but is extended over vastly greater distances. The chance of producing a chain reaction in the surrounding water must be negligible when one considers the ingenuity and care that is taken to insure the chain reaction within the confines of the bomb itself.

Actually the main features of the underwater explosion could be calculated rather accurately. What was uncertain was the reaction of the forces on some of the target vessels. It seemed possible that missiles torn from the target ships might be hurled for considerable distances and so endanger the active fleet.

When the explosion took place, the energy released turned the bomb into a highly compressed gas at a very high temperature. The high temperature spread to the surrounding water to form large quantities of steam and the highly compressed center originated pressure waves which spread through the water in all directions. Part of the wave blew upward and formed the gigantic column of steam and water that made the Baker blast magnificently beautiful. Part of the pressure wave travelled downward, tore loose portions of the lagoon bottom and was reflected upward to aid in producing the column.

The main column was about one-half mile in diameter and the top rose to about one mile. From low-level photographs it appears to be a solid mass of water with vertical sides but actually much of it was steam, water vapor, and spray and the center was probably hollow. The total mass of water raised above the level of the lagoon exceeded one million tons. Fig. 4–1 (p. 95) shows a portion of the column at about the time of maximum development. The plume, a cap of spray that extended beyond the main column, is out of view beyond the top of the picture.

Some of the shock wave energy was transmitted to the air to produce a wave of compression followed by a wave of expansion. At the expansion a beautiful fleeting cloud of condensed water vapor was produced. It is interesting to note that much of the research leading to the development of the bomb had been done with similar clouds produced in chambers a foot or so in diameter. The cloud from the bomb itself was about three miles in diameter.

The initial flash of radiation, so destructive to the people of Hiroshima and Nagasaki, was almost completely absorbed by the water. A high percentage of the gamma rays were absorbed and converted to other, less penetrating forms of radiation. The neutrons were captured by the sodium, chlorine, and other constituents of sea water to form radioactive atoms whose radiations added to those from the fission products. Thus in the underwater burst one of the most prominent features of the air burst was almost completely missing.

THE BASE SURGE

Within a few seconds of its formation the column started to fall back to the surface of the lagoon. This resulted in a wave that looked like solid water but actually was mist and vapor which formed near the base of the original column and then moved outward. This base surge had an initial height of several hundred feet and was an impressive sight, speeding across the lagoon surface at fifty miles an hour. Many observers on ships just outside the atoll, not realizing the nebulous character of the base surge, had a few anxious moments until it decreased sharply in height and finally spent itself on the shores of the atoll.

In its initial phases the base surge towered well above the masts of the largest ships and as it rolled over them all weather surfaces were drenched with sea water. In Fig. 4–2 (p. 96) the base surge is not fully developed but is already several times as high as the ships about to be enveloped in it. If the base surge had been a solid wall of water, as it appeared, much more severe damage would have been done to the above waterline structures. Radioactivity was the only punch carried by the base surge.

The water column and hence the base surge contained nearly all of the radioactive fission products formed by the chain reaction and as the spray advanced over the target ships they were thoroughly contaminated with radioactive products. It was as if all of the deadly contents of the air burst mushroom had been concentrated into one gigantic fall-out that covered a limited area instead of being dispersed in the vastness of the stratosphere.

The contamination left by the base surge proved to be very annoying at Bikini. The high levels of radioactivity prevented safe access to many of the target vessels for some time and the cleanup of the radioactive mess consumed much time and labor. If a city were exposed to the base surge from an underwater burst bomb, a similar situation would obtain. Every exposed surface would receive a deposit of radioactive fission products and with the ordinary types of building construction a considerable amount of contamination would undoubtedly seep inside. Most of the surfaces on the target ships were painted metal and the fission products stuck to these with annoying tenacity. Porous materials such as canvas were so thoroughly saturated and contaminated that cleaning was impossible and ultimate disposal was burial at sea. Even in a modern city, the proportion of porous materials is much greater than on a fighting ship and the problems of decontamination would be correspondingly greater.

There is no doubt that a city exposed to a full-blown base surge such as developed at Bikini would be badly contaminated. However, the production of an effective base surge requires rather special conditions. Without deep water close to the target structures the chance of producing a serious contamination seems doubtful.

JULY 26, 1946

A cautious re-entry of the lagoon was made a few hours after the detonation. Radio-controlled drone boats were sent through the target area and reported the radioactivity to the mother ships by radio. Water samples collected by these boats were rushed to the laboratory for analysis. The drones were closely followed by manned boats which moved cautiously toward the target area. Radioactivity was detectable but not dangerous except near the target area and downwind from it. From this information and a knowledge of the lagoon currents future conditions could be accurately predicted. As a result of these predictions, the active fleet moved into the lagoon on the afternoon of the explosion, ready for work next day.

Two capital ships were missing. The 26,000 ton battleship *Arkansas* had vanished into the initial spray and mist and was never seen again. Moored at something more than 500 feet from the center, she had received such severe underwater damage from the terrific blast wave that she sank almost instantly. The 33,000 ton carrier *Saratoga* went down seven and one-half hours after the blast. She had been mortally wounded in spite of her very rugged construction and compartmentation. The final toll was nine ships sunk and many damaged out of a total of more than eighty.

Radiation surveys soon revealed the actual conditions. Most of the lagoon water was contaminated but the concentrations were not dangerously high over most of the area. The most distant target ships were not seriously damaged, showed little radioactivity, and were promptly reboarded. Ships inside of one mile, however, presented a real hazard. Although relatively undamaged, they had received the full effect of the base surge and were so radioactive that dangerous doses would have been received had they been boarded the first day. Immediate reboarding was out of the question. The radioactivity would decay with time but some of the ships would need attention before decay alone would reduce the activity to safe levels.

Vigorous decontamination measures were initiated. At first these consisted only of washing down the decks with powerful streams of water. Later, as the ships could be approached more closely, other methods were used. Progress was slow. A ship would be "cooled" so that it could be boarded for one hour; later this time would be extended to two, four, and eight hours and eventually twenty-four hour occupation would be possible.

RESIDUAL RADIOACTIVITY

The distinction between the Bikini operation and a wartime situation must be made clear. Bikini was essentially a *safe* operation. All tests and experiments, no matter how important, were conducted under the restrictions of normal, peacetime regulations governing exposure to radioactivity. This was an eminently correct procedure which did not seriously hamper the conducting of experiments nor the recovery of data. The public was not psychologically prepared to accept large scale contacts with radioactivity. Several men died for a variety of reasons at Bikini and were scarcely mentioned; *if even one had been seriously injured by radioactivity public criticism would have been severe.* During wartime almost any operation involves some unusual risk and it is necessary to balance the risk against the possible gains from a successful result before the risk is accepted.

At Bikini the allowable daily radiation dose was set at 0.1 roentgen (a term to be discussed later) which is the accepted maximum allowable daily dose for persons who work with the radiations for long periods of time. Undoubtedly this level could have been greatly exceeded during the Bikini operation with no untoward effects.

The radiation hazards that existed after the Baker test must be evaluated in terms of two standards. According to peacetime standards, many of the ships were too hot to be boarded for many days or weeks. According to the exigencies of a wartime operation, the majority of the ships would have continued in service unless they had been knocked out by the blast. Many of the civilians and the military at Bikini had had no previous experience with radioactive materials or had worked only with the small quantities available before the war. Because of their past experiences and a general awe of the enormous quantities released by the bomb, they over-reacted and tended to exaggerate the hazards but on some ships the radiation hazards were great according to any standard. Many men would have received lethal doses if they had been aboard at the time of the blast.

An underwater burst is a potent weapon against massed ships. Many ships can be sunk, and many more so damaged that much work would be required to make them operable. It does not appear, however, that an appreciable number would be so highly contaminated that they could never be used again. Within a week after the Baker test the lagoon water showed radioactivity less than the maximum allowable and small boats and working parties could move about freely without danger. The radioactivity from an underwater burst in a river or a harbor with large tide flows would be dispersed even more rapidly.

THE ALPHA HAZARD

When an atomic explosion is terminated by the blowing apart of the bomb, some of the original material is left in its unfissioned state. These atoms emit alpha particles, have a relatively long life, and are thoroughly mixed with the fission products by the violence of the explosion. Thus in a contaminated area an appreciable alpha particle hazard exists, in addition to the beta particle and gamma ray hazards. Alpha particles have a very short range and are scarcely a hazard as long as they are outside the body but if they once gain entrance the consequences are apt to be serious. Some radium dial painters during World War I ingested quantities of radium measured only in millionths of a pound, yet many died as a result of the alpha particle bombardment of the body structures.

The Bikini target ships were contaminated with alpha particle emitters and time alone would not appreciably lessen the hazard—the decay in activity will be negligible during a human lifetime. What then is the magnitude of this hazard? Even with the best known decontamination procedures some of the active material will remain to be released by future operations such as sandblasting or welding. This is a difficult hazard to evaluate but from the data on hand it does not appear to be a serious one. Absorbent materials which can not be decontaminated should be disposed of under carefully controlled conditions. Nonporous surfaces should be thoroughly cleaned until they meet certain predetermined standards. Inaccessible places must not be neglected even though much labor is involved. Sometimes elaborate ventilating systems must be dismantled and replaced to avoid the possibility that trapped alpha emitters may shake loose at a later date and enter the room air.

With suitable precautions there seems to be no reason why structures exposed to contamination from the bomb need to be abandoned because of a residual alpha hazard. Unusual operations such as welding may indeed vaporize small quantities of the alpha emitters and some of these may be inhaled or may enter cuts and abrasions. If a reasonable decontamination procedure has been carried out the amount released will be small, all that may enter the body will not be retained, and presumably the exposure will occur at infrequent intervals. Thus the situation is quite different from that of workers who spend several hours each working day exposed to the possible inhalation of alpha emitters.

Two years after the Bikini tests, the Navy sunk some of the remaining target vessels that had been retained for long-time studies. These sinkings served to revive stories of the uninhabitable ships, forever forbidden to men because of their contact with the atom bomb. Such tales must be placed with those that predicted that Hiroshima and Nagasaki would be unfit for human habitation for many decades. The Navy has regularly used over-age ships for target practice and they chose to so use the last of the Bikini fleet. It is probable that economic considerations dictated the final disposition. It is certain that the ships were not centers of radioactive pestilence fatal to all who came on board.

Time is a great asset in reducing most radiation hazards.

The long-lived alpha emitters are an exception to this but most of the fission products decay rapidly with time. The composite mixture of many fission products follows more nearly a 1/time law. To see how this works, assume that at one minute after the explosion the total amount of radioactivity was equivalent to that from one hundred tons of radium. At ten minutes the activity would be ten equivalent tons, at one thousand minutes one-tenth of a ton, and so on. At the end of one year, which is equal to something over 500,000 minutes, the original activity would be reduced to about one-tenth of an equivalent pound. Even with the concentrated deposition which occurred in Test Baker, the beta and gamma hazards decreased to reasonable values in one year. Some of the Bikini ships had outlived their usefulness as test specimens not because they were lethal but because decay had reduced the activity to levels too low to measure accurately.

Chapter 5
NUCLEAR RADIATION AND MAN

"Inherent in the bomb and its wartime use there are intrinsic characteristics which provide basis for tremendous psychological effect."
—Captain George M. Lyon, u.s.n.r.

Radioactivity was not invented by the Manhattan Project. Roentgen, in 1895, announced the production of x-rays and in 1896 Becquerel discovered that uranium minerals emitted something which produced a blackening of photographic plates. The Curies, intrigued by these discoveries, started on the research that led to the discovery of the new elements polonium and radium. From these fundamental results research has advanced step by step and has made possible the large-scale release of nuclear energy.

Some of the biological effects were observed soon after the radiations were discovered and even before they had been identified. The radioactive elements discovered by Madame Curie and her husband were extracted from ores from mines worked commercially for other constituents. Much of this ore came from the Czechoslovakian mines at Joachimstal where the uranium was extensively used for coloring glass and pottery. Miners had been exposed to radioactive materials for many years and under far from ideal working conditions. It had long been known that the life span of the Joachimstal miners was short and that they tended to develop fatal lung congestions but apparently no one became greatly disturbed. It was assumed to be an occupational hazard about which nothing could be done.

As concentrated radioactive materials became available, skin burns were observed on some of the laboratory workers and some crude precautionary measures were taken. In the early days the precautions do not appear to have been considered very seriously—the general feeling seemed to be that since the rays were new and unknown they should be beneficial rather than harmful.

BACKGROUND RADIATION

As methods for detecting the radiations were improved, it became evident that man had been living in the presence of radioactive materials since his creation. Practically all soils and waters contain small amounts of radium or other naturally radioactive elements. Plants absorb some of these elements and thus they are passed on to animals and to man. During his lifetime man gradually acquires radium and since the body tends to store it he has a small but measurable amount fixed in his body at death.

Radium is one of the products formed from the decay of uranium, which is a common constituent of many forms of rocks. The uranium was laid down in these rocks many millions of years ago, and from it countless generations of men have accumulated small amounts of radioactive materials in their bodies. One would like to add—and were none the worse for it—but who can say? Because everyone is exposed, we have no "control" specimens for comparison.

In addition to accumulating radioactive materials in his body, man has been bombarded continuously with cosmic rays. These very penetrating radiations reach the earth from unknown sources in interstellar space. Some cosmic rays are so penetrating that they have been detected beneath several hundred feet of water and in deep mines and consequently man is unable to escape them. Their number is not inconsiderable. It varies with the location on the earth's surface but an average figure would be about twelve per square inch per minute at sea level. The number increases with altitude and will be about eighty times as great at 40,000 feet. In addition, some penetrating radiations are received from small amounts of radioactive elements which are present in practically all substances.

X-RAYS

In addition to the inescapable radiations described, civilized man has accepted with little question the increasing use of x-rays in medical diagnosis and therapy. Frequent chest x-rays are urged for the entire adult population for the purpose of detecting incipient or developed tuberculosis. This campaign is a worthy one and should be encouraged and supported but it must be realized that with each chest x-ray some radiation is absorbed by the body. Similarly, the use of x-rays permits a greatly improved visualization of conditions in the gastrointestinal tract and in bones. Massive doses of radiation are administered in the treatment of various forms of tumors and diseases of the skin.

All of these applications of high-energy radiations are for the purpose of improving the health of the individual and their use should not be discouraged whenever needed. We merely point out that man has accepted widespread uses of radiant energy with none of the emotion with which many greeted the use of the bomb. *Like taxes, radioactivity has long been with us and in increasing amounts; it is not to be hated and feared, but accepted and controlled.*

RADIATION DOSES

The effects of radiation may vary from highly beneficial results in the hands of a competent physician to the rapidly lethal effect of close exposure to an atomic bomb, just as strychnine may be a useful stimulant or a deadly killer. As with medicines, radiation effects vary with the dose administered and it is necessary to establish units of radiation dose if consistent results are to be secured.

Units of radiation are more difficult to establish than a unit of length, weight, or a dose of medicine. The difficulty arises from the fact that the human senses are incapable of detecting the presence of even large amounts of penetrating radiation. As a result of several national and international conferences, a satisfactory unit of radiation was established and appropriately named the roentgen, abbreviated r, after the discoverer of x-rays.

The precise definition of the roentgen is rather technical and need not be given here. It is sufficient to state that the roentgen does not measure the amount of radiation present but rather the amount that is absorbed. An absorption unit is precisely the kind desired, for only the radiation *absorbed* during its passage through the body has a biological effect. That which is not absorbed passes through without effect.

As a result of years of experience, certain levels of dosage have been established to serve as a guide in the safe use of radiation. These established levels are not fixed, immutable laws of nature but are arbitrary values which may change somewhat as further data are obtained. The presently accepted maximum allowable dose over the whole body is 0.1 r per day. This does not mean that any dose below 0.1 r is safe or that anything greater is dangerous. Some types of radiation injury appear to be chance phenomena where the chance increases with the dose received. Exposure to radiation can be compared to the crossing of a busy street intersection. Both are dangerous to an extent determined by the amount of exposure to the hazard.

Workers habitually exposed to radiation are well advised to keep their daily dose as low as is practicable, even though 0.1 r per day appears to be a safe figure. Persons who have received substantially greater single doses must not consider themselves doomed to radiation sickness or early death.

The combined radiation from cosmic rays and naturally occurring radioactive materials amounts to about 0.0002 r per day. This is the inescapable minimum to which all are exposed. The body develops a tolerance to or repairs the damage from this amount of radiation. Workers in special occupations who might receive 0.1 r per day would receive a total of perhaps 30 r per year and will show no ill effects. In 15 years the total dose would be 450 r, an amount which would be almost certainly fatal if received during a single exposure. In the same way, a person who regularly drinks one Martini per day shows no ill effects, but should he drink his year's quota in one day, he would die.

The figures given pertain to the exposure of the whole body to radiation. Much larger doses may be safely administered to small portions of the body. In treating cancer, radiologists may use doses of 5,000 r to a limited volume with no serious effects on the patient. The dose received from a chest x-ray will range from 0.2 to 3.0 r and an examination of the gastro-intestinal system may require 30 r, but the whole body is not exposed.

MEASURING INSTRUMENTS

The establishment of a unit of dose presupposes that means of measurement are available. The first instrument used was the photographic plate by which Becquerel detected the radiations from uranium. Today films are perhaps the most convenient and reliable means of determining total radiation dosage. They are customarily used in the ordinary dental film size, which is easily carried in a pocket or attached to the wrist if it appears that the hand exposure will be greater than that of the whole body. After development the blackening of the film will be a measure of the total exposure during the period the film was worn.

Film processing requires time and it is sometimes desirable to know immediately the amount of exposure. For this purpose pocket ionization chambers or dosimeters have been developed. About the size of a fountain pen, these chambers consist of a small air volume with an insulated electrode. An electric charge placed on this electrode will remain for long periods of time but if radiation enters the chamber the air will become an electrical conductor and some of the charge will leak off. By measuring the loss of electric charge the total dose of radiation can be determined.

Survey instruments or rate meters also depend upon the fact that the penetrating radiation makes a gas conducting. In the Geiger counter, for example, a pulse of electric current will flow through the counter tube when radiation is absorbed in it. This small pulse is amplified to produce the now-famous click which can be heard in a pair of headphones or broadcast from coast to coast. Suitably connected meters will read the average number of pulses received and will thus indicate the rate at which radiation is being received.

Shown in Fig. 5-1 (p. 97) are two monitors at Bikini, using a Geiger counter and an ionization chamber instrument. In Fig. 5-2 (p. 98) a laboratory worker is shown using personnel protection instruments.

Many types of radiation measuring instruments have been devised. Details of their operation need not be discussed here for few will ever be called upon to use them. It is important, however, that reliable, accurate instruments be available for these few. Some of them are expensive but costs will come down with mass production. Such instruments are an indispensable part of an adequate defense against atomic attack, even though the total expense may be large.

RADIATION PSYCHOLOGY

Of the body organs, the human brain is one of the most resistant to the direct effects of radiation but it is *most sensitive
to suggestion and inference*. Through fear and imperfect understanding individuals react to radiation quite out of proportion
to the actual hazards. What is completely unknown and unsus-
pected is not feared. As a consequence, generations have lived
in the presence of cosmic rays and have taken into their bodies
substantial quantities of radioactive materials without the
slightest qualm. Thousands have been exposed to the medical
applications of x-rays without considering them to be poten-
tially dangerous. The Japanese attacks emphasized the fact that
radiation can be a killer and to many it immediately assumed
the nature of a mad dog.

Radiation is dangerous—let there be no mistake about that—
but the modern world abounds in dangerous substances and
situations too numerous to mention. Let us consider only three
of the more common. As a killer, the automobile must be placed
high on the list, claiming as it does over 30,000 lives a year in
the United States alone. This is about three times the number
of deaths from radiation at Hiroshima. Whiskey contains
alcohol, a drug that can kill or maim and one that is frequently
used in medicine to destroy nerve tissue. Finally, tobacco, used
in ever-increasing quantities, contains appreciable amounts of
nicotine, one of the most deadly alkaloids known.

We accept the hazards of the automobile, whiskey, and
tobacco because we are familiar with them and have learned
to use them with some degree of safety. We know how to avoid
killing with the automobile even though we do not always
follow the correct principles. We can distinguish between the
use and the abuse of whiskey and each governs his behavior
according to his desires. Few, indeed, are victims of nicotine
poisoning, although it is quite possible to become one.

To achieve the same rational perspective for radiation, both in peace and in war, the public must be thoroughly informed. *Ignorance must not breed fear nor familiarity contempt.* We are fortunate in having a nucleus of well-trained scientists who have a thorough understanding of radiation hazards and methods of protection against them. We have adequate instrumentation to permit accurate evaluation of any radiation hazards that may exist. We know something about the effects of radiation on the body and are studying methods by which borderline cases may be tided over during the critical period and started on the road to recovery. When the true facts are widely known we should be able to avoid both the Scylla of fear and the Charybdis of contempt and consider radiation as something to be treated with respect, avoided whenever practicable, and accepted when inevitable.

Any general program of education must be planned and carried out with great care. Knowledge is actually an individual interpretation of information presented. Two individuals exposed to the same set of facts may interpret them quite differently and react to them in almost opposite ways. This has been a common experience in indoctrinating large bodies of men in the fundamentals of radiation hazards. As practical experience is gained, the extreme reactions tend to approach the more normal average. The general public will have little opportunity to gain experience with radiation before they may be exposed to a full-scale attack. To avoid mass hysteria and mob confusion, the true situation must be presented factually and unemotionally until the average citizen accepts radiation in its proper perspective.

THE AMERICAN REACTION

The cities of continental United States have never been subjected to bombing or any other form of attack with modern weapons. Consequently, it is very difficult to gauge public reaction to an atomic attack. This is a very important point because public behavior can greatly aid or hamper rescue work

after an atomic disaster. Any public reaction is influenced, if
not completely determined, by the temperament of the people
and their emotional background. The Japanese had a fanatical,
religious devotion to the Emperor and accepted adversity as
something to be endured for his sake. Germans stood up under
a tremendous weight of bombs either because they believed in
the eventual triumph of the Nazi arms or because they were
used to a regimented, regulated regime and accustomed to
doing as they were told.

None of these factors is present in the American picture.
Americans have been accustomed to leading highly independent
lives, doing much as they pleased, and admitting fanatical devotion to no one. How will such a group stand up under a
sudden atomic attack or long-sustained bombings? The answer
is not certain but a few pertinent observations are not encouraging.

On the night of October 30, 1938 Orson Welles broadcast
"The War of the Worlds" the story by H. G. Wells in which
bands of Martians landed and carried all before them until they
were finally overcome by earthly bacteria. Even giving Mr.
Welles due credit for an extremely realistic performance, it
seems incredible that such a furore as ensued could have been
created. As the Martian invaders waded across the Hudson
river on their way to attack New York City, thousands of
citizens rushed into the streets in the utmost confusion or
jumped into their cars to flee—no matter in what direction!
Incidents of individual and mass hysteria were reported from
all parts of the country. Few offered their services to constituted
authority to assist in repelling intruders who appeared to
threaten their most sacred possessions—home and family.

Again consider the public record in reporting flying missiles.
Saucers, discs, space ships, and all manner of flying objects
have been reported by large numbers of reputable citizens to
be doing all manner of things which defy all the ordinary laws

of physics. These reports are a great credit to the public imagination but not to its stability.

These reports of public over-reaction are disturbing but there is other, more optimistic evidence. When well-recognized disasters such as fire or flood have struck at communities in the United States the public behavior has been exemplary. Almost everyone has rallied to meet the common enemy and deeds of heroism have been common. Goods and assistance of all kinds poured in from other areas and reconstruction was soon under way.

The key to the problem is the individual. General rules of procedure can be laid down but without individual co-operation such rules will be ineffective. Public reaction after an attack will be exemplary in proportion to the public understanding of the situation.

From the meager evidence, it seems certain that the American public can be counted on for a stout defense against any threat which they can understand and with which they can grapple. This leaves unanswered the question as to the reaction against sudden atomic attack, for the public is not yet acquainted with the hazards of radioactive warfare and much depends on how the necessary information is imparted.

Chapter 6
THE BOMBING OF GERMANY

"Given enough time, the enemy can recover from anything. Before destruction begins to affect front-line strength, it must, as a rule, cut through considerable and sometimes enormous layers of fat."
-GEN. H. H. ARNOLD

In a book about atomic bombs, it may strike the reader as a curious digression to discuss the bombing of Germany. There are, however, lessons to be learned from the bombardment of German cities and facilities. One very obvious thing was summed up by the U. S. Strategic Bombing Survey when they said, "The great lesson to be learned in the battered towns of England and the ruined cities of Germany is that the best way to win a war is to prevent it from occurring." By considering the air war over Germany we can gain some idea of the effectiveness of strategic bombing and of the ability of a nation to withstand an all-out air attack, keeping in mind a comparison of damage from conventional bombs and from atomic bombs.

Let us look back to the period before the last war. Air power, used so little in World War I, was in its ascendancy. The Italian

52

air strategist, General Douhet, championed the use of the air weapon for a predominant role in any future war. In his classic book "The Command of the Air" Douhet foresaw the use of mass formations of heavy bombers. He recognized the need for gaining command of the air over enemy territory before the offensive air attack could be truly effective. Others, following in Douhet's footsteps, advocated complete dependence upon airpower. They argued that war could be fought high above land-locked armies. A short war was pictured—a war which would play havoc with urban areas and which would render cities uninhabitable; a war in which the enemy could be knocked out by the Bomber Command.

Then Hitler's orders set the German war machine into action. Goering unleased squadrons of Stuka dive bombers upon terrified troops. The Germany Army rolled forward, paced by its devastating Air Arm. Nothing could stop it and nothing did until it reached the English Channel . . . but Goering's Luftwaffe kept right on going across the narrow stretch of water to bomb the British Isles. In the same year that France fell, Germany launched an all-out air offensive against Britain. Starting in August of 1940, wave after wave of German bombers roared across the Channel to harass the beleaguered isle. One need not recount the magnificent way in which the British responded in their hour of crisis. Time after time, Hurricanes and Spitfires rose to meet the invader. Even though outnumbered, the fighters never gave up their heroic part in the Battle for Britain. The men and women of Britain stoically withstood the impact of the continued bombardment. Finally, only a few months after it started, the air attack faltered. Goering had met his first defeat in the fateful year of the greatest of Germany's triumphs.

Air power had met its first rebuff. Appropriately enough, it had succumbed to enemy air action . . . it had proved to be its own worst enemy. It is hard to see from their continued air policy that the Germans learned much from their failure to subdue England. It is not clear that the Allies fully appreciated the significance of the defeat. But air power had not been decisive and war could not neglect the land-sea forces of the past.

STRATEGIC BOMBING

Let us momentarily consider the subject of strategic bombing. First of all, it will be well to define what is meant by strategic bombing. How does it differ from tactical bombing? Realizing that no two authorities will be in perfect agreement, we define strategic bombing as the air operation conducted against an enemy's industrial and manpower resources. By tactical bombing we mean the operation aimed directly at the enemy's forces-in-being, that is, troop concentrations, transportation facilities, and that fraction of industry whose output is necessary for the day-by-day operation of the war machine.

Now that we have defined strategic bombing, let us see what its objectives are in terms of targets for attack. First we list prime sources of raw materials, such as oil fields, coal deposits, and associated facilities. Next we have the industries which are used to convert these raw materials; these are the process industries, such as ore reduction plants. Then there are the basic industries which fabricate these processed materials into heavy goods such as tanks and cannon, and the light industries which include aircraft assembly plants and factories for producing electrical equipment. Finally, and by no means the least important, we come to the civilian manpower necessary for the operation of these industries.

Each type of industrial installation presents a different kind of target to enemy air action. Some are relatively invulnerable, whereas others are easily put out of commission by light damage. We shall not attempt to treat the operational problem of analyzing a target for attack except to point out how much different a conventional bombing raid is from an atomic attack.

For conventional bombing, the problem can be looked upon as a priority assignment job. In a given area there will be a certain number of plants. Together they may be worth launching a raid of, say, 500 heavy bombers. Within the target system individual targets are allocated 10%, 20%, or even 50% of the total bomb tonnage to be dropped. Depending upon the nature of the target and the kind of opposition to be expected, the raid is protected by an appropriate number of fighter planes. The nature of the target may dictate bombing with incendiaries or with a particular type of high-explosive bomb.

In the case of an atomic attack there is a severe limitation. First, the target has to be "worth" the expenditure of one atomic bomb. If the target is a small factory located several miles from a critical industry, it may not be worth an atomic bomb. But if the target merits receiving an atomic bomb, we cannot expect to send a single bombing plane on the mission. Nor can we send just two or three bombers, as was done at Hiroshima. The risk is now too great. If enemy action against a 500-plane conventional raid brings down 10% of the bombers, the tonnage delivered to the target is still very high. If the enemy should happen to hit the A-bomber the raid would be over. For this reason the A-bomber would have to be accompanied by planes to act as decoys. Six or even a dozen decoys might be needed per mission and if the decoys are B–36s, such a mission will be costly both in money and effort. But let us return to the age of the B–17s that bombed Germany in the last war.

GERMANY UNDER BOMBARDMENT

The United States was given a "go-ahead" on military aircraft production in mid-1940. When we entered the war on December 7th, 1941, our production had not increased by a large factor and did not rise to what we can call a "victory level" until two years later. The production figures shown graphically in Fig. 6–1 are of more than historical interest to national security. It took the United States many months to produce heavy bombers in quantity. Thus it was that Germany did not really take a beating from the air until early in 1944.

Somewhat earlier the British had undertaken some 1,000 plane attacks on German cities, but these had not been sustained. A few had done terrific damage, particularly at Hamburg. One raid set the city ablaze and thousands perished in the fire storm that followed. *More died at Hamburg than were killed at Nagasaki by the atomic bomb.* In fact, the damage done at

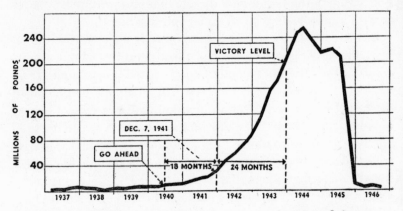

Fig. 6-1   Military aircraft production in the United States.

Hamburg was equal to that from two atomic bombs; the ruins of the city are grim testimony to this equivalence.

The story of the Allied strategic bombing of Germany is told in Fig. 6-2A, where we have plotted the tons of bombs delivered on Germany throughout the war. To say that our bombers dumped over 1,360,000 tons of bombs on Germany scarcely conveys the magnitude of the effort or does credit to the courage of the airmen who took the bombs to their destinations in the face of fierce enemy resistance, nor do the figures depict the tremendous havoc wrought by the bombs. Some concept of this damage is given by the photograph in Fig. 6-3 (p. 99). This also illustrates the tremendous waste involved in strategic bombing, for if a bomb completely misses its target it sometimes does absolutely no damage to the enemy. In urban areas, of course, bombs which miss their target spill over

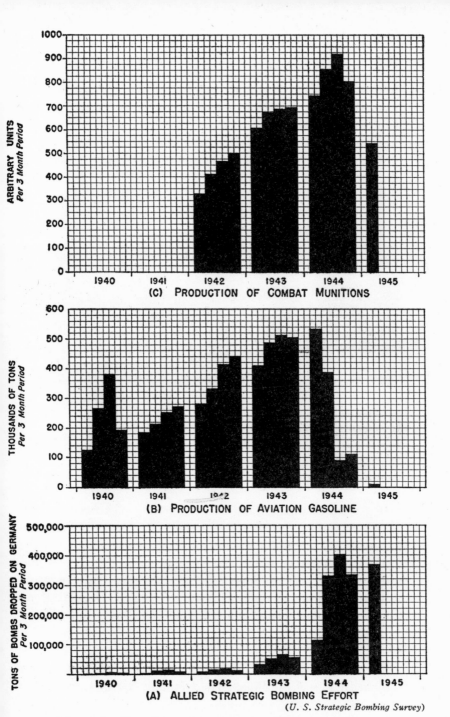

Fig. 6–2   The effects of strategic bombing on Germany.

into populated areas and are not wasted. Figs. 6–4A and 6–4B
(pp. 100, 101) show urban areas after heavy raids with conventional bombs.

The damage from a high explosive bomb cannot be appreciated merely by looking at the crater which it makes in
the earth when it explodes. A more graphic way to visualize
the damage is to show the destruction of buildings of ordinary
dwelling-type construction. In Fig. 6–5 we have illustrated the

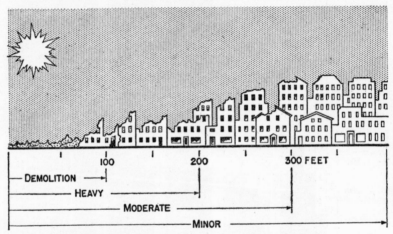

Fig. 6–5   Blast damage from a two-ton High-Explosive bomb.

extent of the damage done by the bursting of a two-ton H.E.
(High-Explosive) bomb at roof height. Degrees of damage are
indicated as demolition, severe, moderate, and minor. Only the
latter two types of bomb damage are subject to repair and
reuse of the dwelling. Severe damage requires that the structure be torn down or undergo major rebuilding. Demolition, as
the word implies, leaves the structure completely unusable.

EFFECTS ON GERMAN INDUSTRY

Some of the more vital industries were located deep within
the boundaries of the Reich. The Germans felt that some were

so distant from the border that an enemy would not be able to penetrate successive layers of defense to reach them. Germany attempted to use its limited space as an ally. She was partially successful, even though the Allies developed long-range escort fighters and armored the B–17 flying fortress so that more distant targets could be hit. Vital industries located close to foreign soil were ringed with strong defenses. The city of Schweinfurt, for example, contained the heart of Germany's antifriction bearing industry. It was here that the Reich concentrated its ball-bearing plants and because of their importance to the Wehrmacht, the city was strongly defended. The Allies staged a mass raid on Schweinfurt early in the air war. Over 200 heavy bombers struck at the city but they had to engage in a series of air battles from the time they crossed the Channel. Only a few of these planes came out of the battle unscathed and more than 62 were shot down. Despite the strong defensive measures, which caused us a heavy loss of bombers, the enemy was struck a damaging blow. Quick to appreciate their peril should the Wehrmacht be denied ball bearings, the Reich dispersed the industry to other locations and it soon was producing at a pre-raid level. Again and again, the Germans demonstrated a stubbornly tenacious ability to recover from damaging air attacks. In the case of the ball-bearing industry, production was never again interfered with in the course of the war.

Not all industries could be uprooted and relocated in safe places, or put underground. The huge hydrogenation plant at Leuna, for example, was doomed to be a prime target for continued air attack. The attacks on the refineries were intensified at the end of the war and produced a drastic reduction in the supply of high octane gas for the Luftwaffe. Fig. 6–2B illustrates the decisive effect of bombing on aircraft gasoline production. Although the sustained air attacks against the petroleum industry were undertaken late in the war, they paid quick dividends. The flow of critical aviation fuel was finally reduced

to a mere trickle; this had an immediate effect upon the activities of the Luftwaffe. In marked contrast, the production
of German fighter planes actually increased during the intense
aerial bombardment; this fact has been taken by some as in-
dicating that the air bombardment was ineffective. No one
production item can be singled out as a criterion of the effectiveness or noneffectiveness of strategic bombing. Necessity is
the mother of invention and if the Germans desperately needed
fighter planes (and they did) they would most certainly concentrate upon production of these in preference to other war
material. It is true, however, that the overall German war production was remarkably high during the air bombardment and
did not drop off until the end of 1944. For example, combat
munitions, such as ammunition, "panzer" tanks, naval vessels,
and aircraft, stayed at a fairly high level throughout the first
nine months of the air attack (see Fig. 6–2C). The break came
early in 1945 and only two months later the total production
figures had dwindled to about one-half the peak value. Germany had not been knocked out from the air but she had been
seriously weakened.

Once our bombing was directed against particular German
industries, such as gasoline production, it produced decisive
effects, but against other targets the showing was poor. The
Germans were quick to improvise, to make substitute materials,
to repair plant damage, and to convert plants to new types of
production. Then, too, they were not hard pressed until late in
the war. They had excess capacity in many of their plants and
time after time proved that Allied Intelligence was inaccurate
so far as estimates of production capability were concerned.

ATOMIC BOMBS ON GERMANY

Recently there have been attempts to show that the atomic
bomb is not a terribly powerful weapon by pointing out that
it is equivalent to one thousand TNT bombs of the one-ton
size and that the results of bombing Germany with over a mil-

lion tons of such bombs did not cause capitulation. The argument is that Germany received the equivalent of a large number of atomic bombs and still kept producing a steady flow of war goods. In comparing atomic bombs with conventional ones, there are a number of striking differences to consider. First let us ask, "How many atomic bombs would it take to produce the same damage that was inflicted on Germany by TNT bombs?" Obviously, the answer will be an estimate only, for many isolated targets hit by TNT bombs would not be worth an A-bomb. *A-bombs are too big for many military applications.* Instead of one bomb equivalent to 20,000 tons of TNT, it would be more useful to have a number of bombs of smaller size, but it has been repeatedly pointed out that the A-bomb has a definite minimum size.

The comparison of a Nagasaki-type bomb to 20,000 tons of high explosive is made in terms of a huge pile of TNT located at one point. If this pile is divided into small portions and spread over an area of a few square miles, the total damage will be far greater than if the big pile were exploded. To equal the damage from an atomic bomb with ordinary one-ton bombs, dropped over the same area, it is not necessary to use 20,000 of them. The same result might be secured with only 2,000 of the smaller bombs. Much would depend upon the type of target; fewer incendiaries might produce just as much damage.

Calculation of the number of atomic bomb equivalents delivered on Germany must be adjusted for several factors—such as overhitting, the paralyzing effect of the instantaneous blow at many facilities, the more difficult task of repair, and the problem of bombing accuracy. It appears that about 75 atomic bombs would have done the same damage to target areas in Germany as was done by all the strategic bombing during the last war. In addition, at least 200,000 tons of ordinary bombs would be required to account for the areas which would not be worth an atomic bomb. Seventy-five atomic bombs delivered on target might mean that 100 or more would have to be launched.

This is by no means an inconsiderable number of weapons, especially for a country which may have a limited supply of uranium or inadequate production facilities.

The estimate of 75 A-bombs is based upon a comparison of the physical damage and not upon the number of people killed. A tremendous loss of life in German cities could have been caused with far fewer than 75 bombs if the cities were not alerted at the time of the raid. About one-fourth of Germany's population was concentrated in 25 cities of more than one-quarter million people. If the cities were alerted and had adequate shelters, the loss of life would not have been excessive and even 75 bombs would not have killed more than about one million people. On the other hand, the blast effect would render much of the populace homeless and leave industry without facilities.

On this reasoning, we can conclude that *a properly prepared and alerted country can absorb not a huge but a fair number of A-bombs.* We have failed to properly consider one important difference between atomic and TNT bombs—the property of *saturation.* If 100 one-ton TNT bombs are dropped on a large industrial area the bombs will scatter and some places will be untouched. With an atomic bomb, however, the action is not so irregular. The A-bomb spares little and wrecks the area so thoroughly that we say it saturates it. Additional bombing would produce little if any extra damage near the bomb burst. Under such conditions it is impossible to repair facilities and start up production the next day or the next month. After absorbing 75 A-bombs, Germany would not have been a very productive nation. Furthermore, since this destruction could conceivably be delivered in the space of *days* rather than *months,* it is clear that atomic bombs lend new possibilities to warfare.

The evidence in Germany indicates that a properly prepared country can absorb terrific punishment and still keep going. It can even absorb more than just a few atomic bombs. But if a nation possesses the ability to deliver, say, 100 A-bombs *on target,* then the story may be quite different especially if the raids are closely spaced. From the German experience with dispersion of certain critical industries it is clear that this defense measure was effective. If a country could afford to disperse its largest cities and industries, it is quite possible that even 100 A-bombs would not cause capitulation. Much, of course, would depend on that intangible—the will of the people to resist. No country confronted with the threat of atomic bombardment and possessed of the will to survive will overlook a single protective measure that will lessen the effect of the bombing. As we shall see, such measures do exist and will provide a real degree of protection, but before we discuss this matter, let us look at the bombing of Japan, where atomic bombs were actually used as military weapons.

Chapter 7
THE DESTRUCTION OF JAPAN

"Might not a bomb no bigger than an orange be found to possess a secret power to destroy a whole block of buildings—nay, to concentrate the force of a thousand tons of cordite and blast a township at a stroke?"
—WINSTON CHURCHILL *Thoughts and Reflections* (1925)

The electrifying headlines "JAPS STRIKE AT PEARL HARBOR" now seem long ago and far away. But on that Sunday afternoon in December of 1941 the United States was catapulted into the costliest war in its history.

The war necessarily had to be waged at a great distance from the Americas. Two huge oceans intervened between us and our Axis foes. We have already viewed a part of the war in Europe. Germany did not collapse under sustained heavy bombardment from the air but she was considerably softened by it. After months of daily punishment, Germany still fought on, but she was a nation that bled from every pore—a nation in the last desperate throes of determined resistance. Now let us look at Japan and see how she fared under our attack.

64

Everyone in the Pentagon and the man in the street knew that our forces would have to strike at the home island of Japan before the enemy in the Pacific could be defeated. To accomplish this, the United States was faced with the most difficult delivery problem imaginable. There were no close-in bases from which our bombers could take off to bombard Tokyo and the other arsenals of Japan. Furthermore, our sea power in the Pacific was almost nonexistent. The Pearl Harbor disaster had weakened our naval might and little could be spared from the Atlantic. But while our surface fleet was being repaired and augmented for the day when it would avenge Pearl Harbor, the undersea fleet went to work.

THE STRANGLEHOLD

Thousands of miles of open water protected Japan from Allied arms. Our B–17s and B–24s were unable to strike at the target for lack of bases within range of Japan. Not so with the submarines that slipped through the vastness of the Pacific, ranging far from their home bases to strike at the lifeline of Japan—the Emperor's ships. These were rich targets, loaded with troops outbound and inbound with strategic materials from newly won island outposts.

In the first year of the war in the Pacific, while our forces struggled to halt the Nipponese aggression, submarine warfare accounted for 134 ship sinkings totaling over one-half million tons. The next year the submarine pack was stronger and more deadly, chalking up a score of 284 ships, for a total of over a million tons, and in the crucial year of 1944 our undersea craft took a toll of almost 500 ships. To the total tonnage sunk by subs, carrier aircraft, the surface fleet, and land-based aircraft added an almost equal contribution, for a total of about nine million tons of enemy shipping destroyed. When we consider that Japan started the war with about 6 million tons and added about 4 millions during the war, it is clear that the home island was effectively cut off from its empire. The destruction of the merchant fleet was a stranglehold slowly applied to the economic windpipe of Japan.

Even before the air attack began, the rising sun of the Empire had begun to set. Stock piles of strategic materials dwindled. Coal, ore, and petroleum imports were reduced to a trickle. Japanese industry soon found itself with raw materials in short supply. In the summer of 1944, Tojo's rule in Japan ended. He had assumed office shortly before Pearl Harbor and had reigned supreme through the war years; his fall was an indication that all was not well with Japan. Within Japanese official circles there was awareness of impending disaster. Admiral Takagi had systematically reviewed the course of events and had concluded that Japan could not win the war which she had perpetrated so treacherously. Then began the Japanese effort to seek a way out. But the war was to continue for some time. The home island had not yet felt the sting of the B–29; with its appearance, Japan could no longer conceal the shattered state of its military machine.

THE SUPERFORTRESS

The story of the B–29 begins in the prewar years when far-sighted men recognized the need for long-range, high payload bombers. Staggering as were the requirements, the aircraft industry tackled the job. Design changes were continuous and not until a year after Pearl Harbor were 3 prototypes flight tested. Two years later, B–29s were rolling off production lines in huge factories specially constructed for their fabrication.

Since it was clear that the huge ship would operate over ranges too great to be accompanied by fighter craft, it was outfitted with heavy defensive armament. Lessons learned over Germany with its predecessor, the B–17, were used to make the B–29 into a flying battleship of the sky. Everything about the B–29 is big. We have tabulated some of the vital statistics in Fig. 7–1. It is composed of 137,000 different kinds of parts, which gives some indication of the maintenance problem which was faced to keep the huge ships in flying condition. Before island bases were taken, the now famous Twentieth Bomber Command was organized. Crews for this new Com-

WHAT IT TAKES TO KEEP
A B-29 IN COMBAT

AIR CREW 14

OPERATIONS 18

MAINTENANCE 20

TRANSPORTATION 8

ADMINISTRATION 13

HOUSEKEEPING 12

TOTAL 85 { 12 OFFICERS
73 ENLISTED PERSONNEL

(From U. S. Air Forces)

Fig. 7–1

mand were trained at B–29 bases in the wheatfields of Kansas and there the kinks were ironed out of the new plane.

Meanwhile, island-hopping operations in the Pacific were bringing Allied forces closer and closer to the heart of the Empire. Soon there were to be island bases on which 10,000-foot air strips would be laid out to accommodate this newcomer to the Pacific air war. On these tiny islands, won at high cost with American lives, the B–29s would some day roar off to bomb Tokyo. It was to be a touch-and-go operation, for the range of the huge plane was just sufficient; unfavorable winds or a gas-hungry engine might drop the dwindling gas supply until the gage needle fluttered at the EMPTY marker. In such exigencies, crews were trained to bail out and an alert air-sea rescue operation would seek them in the endless expanse of ocean.

THE AIR ASSAULT

Early in the war, General Doolittle led a special striking force of carrier-based bombers in the first raid on Japan. Despite its sensational aspect, the raid did little damage, but as a harbinger of things to come it must have instilled fear into the Japanese war lords. Other than this early raid and a few small scale raids staged from China, the home island of Japan remained virgin territory for air action.

The first B–29 raids took place in the early summer of 1944. These were on a fairly small scale and it was not until the next year that mass formations of heavy bombers appeared over Japan. At first, the B–29s flew high—30,000 feet above sea level. At this altitude, bombing was not accurate, even with trained bombardiers and improved bombsights. Only about 1 bomb in 10 found its target. There was little evidence of the much publicized "pickle-barrel" bombing. A bombardier releasing a bomb at 30,000 feet might expect the bomb to hit somewhere within 300 feet of the target. Under combat conditions, many bombs missed by more than 1000 feet.

A reversal in tactics was made on March 9, 1945. Swarms of B–29s, flying at low altitude where they couldn't miss, attacked four great Japanese cities with incendiary bombs. Low level tactics were then possible because air supremacy over the island had been achieved and even antiaircraft fire was not heavy. The combination of low-level bombing and the use of incendiaries was an unusually effective innovation in the air war. When the last of the B–29s released its deadly bomb load and turned to make the long trip back to the Marianas, Tokyo was ablaze. Caught unprepared and blocked on all sides by walls of flame, the inhabitants perished by the thousands. *Even the later atomic disaster at Hiroshima was less terrible and less destructive than this Tokyo fire raid.* For many, death came quickly. Fires were fanned into a raging inferno by a high wind and lives were snuffed out almost instantly by the furnace-like heat. Grotesque indeed were the bodies of victims hardened in weird postures from instant suffocation. Not until the fires abated could the survivors re-enter the stricken area. Firefighting equipment was ineffective. The holocaust burned itself out, leaving devastation awesome to behold (Fig. 7–2, p. 102). Almost 15 square miles of the world's fourth largest city had been wiped out. This and a few subsequent minor raids took a toll of almost 100,000 lives in the Tokyo area and there were almost as many injured as dead. A new high in mass destruction had been achieved. Not even the atomic bomb was to outclass it. In spite of the extensive damage, Tokyo was not wiped out as a city. It was still very much alive and was, in fact, later considered as a target for the third atomic bomb.

A very significant thing had occurred in this aerial bombardment. Tokyo had been subjected to a "saturation attack," an attack so thorough that no additional bombardment would contribute significantly to the further destruction of the bombed section. It is well to mark this phase of aerial warfare carefully, for it is the principal characteristic of an atomic bomb attack, although it is not always so recognized. Rarely is it possible to achieve saturation with conventional bombs, for the bomb tonnages required are so enormous and bombing accuracy is so erratic that saturation is approached gradually and at terrific expense in the delivery of the weapons. In the case of Tokyo the effect of each incendiary was magnified by the stimulating action of the high wind. In effect, Tokyo had received many times the damage from the raid than would normally have accrued. Never again did the Allies achieve such military success with incendiaries. Other attacks were made in larger number and with high bomb tonnages, yet far fewer people were killed.

We repeatedly stress the number of people killed in Japan because the number was far greater than in Germany. Although the average population density of the two countries was almost exactly the same, Japan was much more highly urbanized. About one-fifth of the population lived in the six cities of Tokyo, Yokohama, Osaka, Kobe, Nagoya, and Kyoto. Even more striking is the fact that three-fourths of all city-dwellers lived in 66 cities.

CITIES AS TARGETS

Tokyo was only one of 66 cities on the target list of the Allied air attack. City after city was systematically subjected to air bombardment. In most cases, incendiaries were used instead of high explosives. The results, while not always as spectacular as the Tokyo fire raid, were most impressive. Cities such as Nagoya, Kobe, and Osaka were struck with mass bombardment. These names hold little significance for Americans and it is surprising to learn that each had a population of over one million people.

When closer bases were secured and more B–29s became available, other Japanese cities shared the fate of the larger targets. Prior to final capitulation, some sixty other cities in Japan had received a total of over 100,000 tons of bombs. The damage done seems all out of proportion to the total number of bombs dropped, especially when we remember the results obtained in Germany. To merely cite dry statistics and say that over 2 million buildings were destroyed, 9 million people made homeless, and so forth, is not to appreciate the magnitude of the disaster which was visited upon Japan. But if we replace the strange, tongue-twisting names of Japanese cities with names of American cities of about the same size, we begin to see more vividly what happened to the little island which had dared to defy the Americans. In Fig. 7–3, we have indicated on a map of the United States the cities which are equivalent to those which were hit in Japan. After each American equivalent, we have given the percentage area of destruction for its Japanese counterpart. This factual chart can not, however, call to mind the scenes of terror that accompanied the incendiary raids. A city under incendiary attack is an awesome sight from the air. It rivals that which an astronomer views when he sights a distant galaxy in his telescope. At first glance, it is difficult to recognize that Fig. 7–4 (p. 103) actually depicts an incendiary attack, so much does it resemble some stellar spectacle. But below this pyrotechnic display is a scene less wondrous. Here the splattering of the incendiaries creates a multitude of fires. Efforts of firefighters to combat the simultaneous outbreak of so many conflagrations are futile; even firebreaks prove of no avail and the final deterrent was usually the lack of combustible material. The damage in many cities was comparable to that inflicted by an atomic bomb.

There is plenty of evidence that the Japanese were thoroughly shaken by the air attack. More than half the population of Tokyo fled the city. In other cities, people streamed out to the country to shake the menace of a threatened raid. It has been estimated that over eight million people left their city homes and took to the roads to seek new shelter. The effect on morale was marked. At last the Japanese people could see at first hand the failure of their war effort. Over one-half million people on the home front were listed as casualties. Japan was mortally wounded, reeling and groggy from sustained air attack. On her production front, critical items were coming from factories in a faltering and scant flow. Here Japan had double trouble. Not only were her factories hampered by lack of raw materials due to strangulation of her shipping, but they were in part crippled by air action and absenteeism of the workers. Japan was on her knees but she was still fighting a fanatical battle. In the home

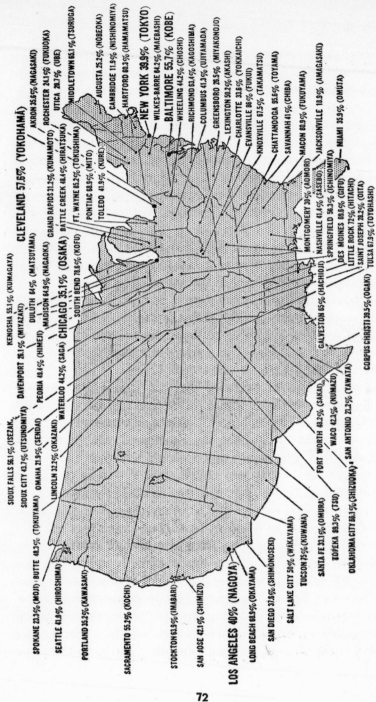

Fig. 7-3 Damage to Japanese cities correlated with American cities.

SIOUX FALLS 56.1% (ISEZAK)

KENOSHA 55.1% (MIYAZAKI)

SIOUX CITY 43.7% (UTSUNOMIYA)

DAVENPORT 26.1% (HIMEJI)

AKRON 35.6% (NAGASAKI)

SPOKANE 23.3% (MOJI) BUTTE 48.3% (TOKUYAMA) OMAHA 21.9% (SENDAI)

DULUTH 64% (MATSUYAMA)

ROCHESTER 24.1% (FUKUOKA)

PEORIA 49.4% (HIMEJI)

MADISON 64.9% (NAGAOKA)

UTICA 20.7% (UBE)

SEATTLE 41.8% (HIROSHIMA)

LINCOLN 32.2% (OKAZAKI)

WATERLOO 44.2% (SAGA)

GRAND RAPIDS 31.2% (KUMAMOTO)

MIDDLETOWN 65.1% (TSURUGA)

BATTLE CREEK 48.4% (HIRATSUKA)

AUGUSTA 25.2% (NOBEOKA)

CHICAGO 35.1% (OSAKA)

FT. WAYNE 85.2% (TOKUSHIMA)

CAMBRIDGE 11.9% (NISHINOMIYA)

PORTLAND 35.3% (KAWASAKI)

SOUTH BEND 78.6% (KOFU)

PONTIAC 68.9% (MITO)

HARTFORD 60.3% (HAMAMATSU)

TOLEDO 41.9% (KURE)

NEW YORK 39.9% (TOKYO)

WILKES-BARRE 64.2% (MAEBASHI)

BALTIMORE 55.7% (KOBE)

WHEELING 44.2% (CHOSHI)

RICHMOND 63.4% (KAGOSHIMA)

COLUMBUS 41.3% (UIYAMADA)

GREENSBORO 26.5% (MIYAKONOJO)

LEXINGTON 50.2% (AKASHI)

CHARLOTTE 33.6% (YOKKAICHI)

EVANSVILLE 86% (FUKUI)

KNOXVILLE 67.5% (TAKAMATSU)

CHATTANOOGA 95.6% (TOYAMA)

SAVANNAH 41% (CHIBA)

MACON 80.9% (FUKUYAMA)

JACKSONVILLE 18.9% (AMAGASAKI)

MIAMI 35.9% (OMUTA)

MONTGOMERY 30% (AOMORI)

NASHVILLE 41.4% (SASEBO)

SPRINGFIELD 56.3% (ICHINOMIYA)

DES MOINES 69.9% (GIFU)

LITTLE ROCK 72% (HITACHI)

SAINT JOSEPH 28.2% (OITA)

TULSA 67.9% (TOYOHASHI)

CORPUS CHRISTI 39.5% (OGAKI)

GALVESTON 65% (HACHIOJI)

FORT WORTH 68.2% (OMURA)

WACO 47.2% (NUMAZU)

SAN ANTONIO 21.2% (YAWATA)

CLEVELAND 57.5% (YOKOHAMA)

SANTA FE 33.1% (TSU)

TOPEKA 69.3% (TSU)

OKLAHOMA CITY 66.1% (SHIZUOKA)

LOS ANGELES 40% (NAGOYA)

LONG BEACH 68.9% (OKAYAMA)

SAN DIEGO 37.6% (SHIMONOSEKI)

SALT LAKE CITY 50% (WAKAYAMA)

TUCSON 75% (KUWANA)

SAN JOSE 42.1% (SHIMIZU)

STOCKTON 63.9% (IMABARI)

SACRAMENTO 55.2% (KOCHI)

72

islands, there were still 2-1/2 million combat troops and 9,000 vicious Kamikaze planes. An invasion would have been perilous, although it is clear now that Japan was in a position very similar to that of Germany just before the latter surrendered. But hindsight gives vision even to the blind.

Many IFs can be posed about the final phases of the war against Japan. IF we had continued our stranglehold on the Japanese lifeline of shipping and denied her access to petroleum, would the bombings have been required for surrender? IF we had bombed transportation targets and vital facilities, would we have had to bomb the cities? IF we had asked for something less than unconditional surrender, could not the war have ended in 1944? To all of these IFs we add the big IF about the atomic bomb. Should it have been used?

From the vantage point of history it is easy to say that the use of the A-bomb was not a military necessity. But we did not know then what we know today. An invasion of Japan had been scheduled for November of 1945. This operation would undoubtedly have been a success. But at what cost! No man knows how many American lives would have been sacrificed on the shores of the home island. Certainly the loss of life would have been staggering. But all of these IFs are answered for us. The A-bomb *was* used and a few days later the war was over. Because of the close coincidence of the two events, it is often assumed that the A-bomb ended the war. In any case, it provided an excuse for Japan to end the war.

THE ATOMIC BOMBINGS

The story of Hiroshima and Nagasaki has been told many times, sometimes more emotionally than factually, and some of the pertinent points often escape emphasis. First, at the time of the bombings we enjoyed complete supremacy of the air over Japan. Second, our A-bomber was subject to what fighter resistance the enemy could muster for only a relatively short distance. In addition, ground defenses at the target were not capable of throwing up an effective antiaircraft barrage and the densely populated city of Hiroshima (and this was true also of Nagasaki) was not alerted at the time of the attack. An earlier alert had sounded but the appearance of only a few bombers was not sufficiently frightening to compel the people to seek cover. It is important to stress these facts because many thousands of people paid with their lives because they failed to seek shelter. In the future, should we use atomic bombs against an enemy, we shall not be dealing with a Hiroshima-like situation. Delivery will be far more difficult.

Many words have been used to describe the power of the atomic bomb. The phrase "20,000 ton H. E. equivalent" has already been explained but it means little to the layman. It is easiest to visualize the power of the bomb in terms of the physical damage done at various distances from ground zero. Everyone has seen photographs of atomic blast damage at Hiroshima but not everyone has studied them with care. Note, for example, the photograph (Fig. 7–5, p. 104) showing bomb damage within a thousand feet of ground zero. In view of the much publicized power of the atomic bomb, is it not strange that there should be even a few buildings left standing this close to the explosion? Actually, the bomb at Hiroshima was detonated high in the air so that its blast effect would spread over a considerable area. Because of this high altitude of detonation, the bomb lost much of its punch before the blast wave struck the ground. Note that a reinforced concrete building is still standing, with its roof still intact, and that the very wide bridge across the river is not even touched. Although the A-bomb saturates a considerable area, it is not an absolute weapon. Apparently some close-in structures can withstand its blast effect.

The atomic bomb is truly a powerful weapon; we do not wish to imply that it is not. On the other hand, it does do only *finite* damage and this fact must be appreciated. Rather than discuss at length the effects of atomic bombs in Japan, it will be more useful to translate the results of these bombings in terms of comparable American cities. In so doing, we must remember that there are differences between American and Japanese cities. Many of the structures so completely smashed at Hiroshima were flimsily built and easily knocked down by a blast wave, but many were well built and modern. Not all American cities are built more ruggedly.

There is one very significant difference between Japanese cities and the great metropolitan areas of our country. In cities like New York and Chicago, such a high value is placed on a small area of ground in the business district that the city has been given a vertical structure. Hundreds of skyscrapers have been built and, more often than not, they have been concentrated in a very small area. Because of this, we shall consider skyscraper cities as special targets for atomic attack.

Chapter 8
THE UNITED STATES UNDER ATTACK

"Here, in the first gaunt years of the Atomic Age lies a country, a continental land mass, more favored by man and nature than any other in history . . ."
—JOHN GUNTHER, *Inside U.S.A.*

Let us now turn our attention to the United States and imagine it to be under atomic attack by a foreign power. One of the most obvious targets might be our huge centers of dense population. Of these, New York's Manhattan and Chicago's Loop head the list. We shall treat these as proving grounds for several hypothetical bomb bursts. This is not done to frighten those who live in these areas, but to assess the peculiar hazards which attend an atomic attack upon such metropolitan centers.

We shall again assume * that one atom bomb is equivalent to 50,000 tons of TNT. This does not imply that such bombs exist but it seems reasonable to assume that they can be developed. Furthermore, this reasoning is in line with a statement made in the Fourth Semiannual Report of the Atomic Energy Commission, where it was said, ". . . the position of the United States

* R. E. Lapp, *Bulletin of the Atomic Scientist*, p. 49 (Feb. 1948).

in the field of atomic weapons has been substantially improved." This is hardly a quantitative statement but size has no particular bearing on our discussion. *Actually, the atomic bomb is already so powerful that it is big enough for all but a very few targets.* Bigger bombs would be wasteful of their energy and as military instruments they would find little application.

To date eight atomic bombs have been exploded and of these only two were detonated as weapons of war. The first test bomb was exploded on a steel tower 100 feet above the New Mexico desert at Alamogordo, two more were detonated at Bikini, and more recently three were tested at Eniwetok Atoll in the Pacific.

Very little has been written about Operation Sandstone (the code used to describe the atomic tests at Eniwetok). Admiral W. S. Parsons, Director of Atomic Defense for the Navy Department, did state that the Baker Test at Bikini was "the only one out of eight atomic bombs fired which has left dangerous amounts of radioactive residue." With regard to this radioactive contamination, Admiral Parsons further stated that ". . . it is by no means established that it would surely occur even as a result of an underwater burst in one of our harbors." Apparently, then, lingering radioactive residue is not an inevitable consequence of an underwater burst.

A HARBOR BURST

Because many of our largest cities are situated close to large bodies of water, the probable effects of an underwater explosion must be studied in some detail in order to assess their magnitude. Many have warned that an enemy might put into one of our ports in a tramp steamer and detonate an atomic bomb stored in its hold. This explosion, they believe, would send a lethal spray of radioactivity over an entire metropolitan area, killing everyone and rendering the region uninhabitable for many years.

The facts indicate that such an attack is rather improbable.

However, an atomic bomb might be delivered by aircraft and exploded by a delayed fuse. Should the technical difficulties inherent in atomic bomb design allow for such delivery, we would have to consider the problem of exact placement of the bomb within the body of water. Consider New York harbor, for example, which is illustrated in Fig. 8–1 (p. 105). On the left is the Hudson River and on the right side of the photograph is the East River. Both these rivers are comparatively narrow and there would be considerable chance that an aerial delivery would fail to land in the center of the river. This would seriously limit the likelihood of a base surge. Even if the bomb did land exactly in the desired spot, there is one factor which up to now we have neglected. Everyone seems to have assumed that our harbors are just like the Bikini lagoon. Such is not the case. The average depth of the Bikini lagoon is 175 feet, whereas there are only a very few harbors in this country which approach that depth. Most American ports are so shallow that they have to be dredged to a depth of 30 or 40 feet to allow passage of ocean-going vessels. It is for this reason that we believe that even a properly placed atomic bomb would not be effective in producing a base surge. *There simply would not be enough water for the surge to be created.*

Even if a base surge could be produced in the Hudson River off downtown Manhattan (and this appears highly improbable), would such a burst kill everyone in New York City? Some seem to think that it would. They apparently forget the results of the test at Bikini, which definitely showed that the range of lethality of the base surge was about one mile under conditions of no wind. With a wind, it might stretch out to two miles in the downwind direction. This would scarcely wipe out all of New York, which covers an area of 365 square miles! However, if a 1 × 2 mile blanket of radioactive mist were to roll over Manhattan, the loss of life would be tremendous. Here again, we must examine our conditions carefully. The broad, unobstructed expanse of Bikini lagoon is not the same kind of surface as that presented by Manhattan's skyline. Along the Battery high buildings rise hundreds of feet into the air. Narrow canyons are formed by the streets between. A base surge trying to roll over this obstacle would meet considerable opposition and we believe that the outer row of buildings along the waterfront would break up and turn back much of the surge, and thus shield the other buildings.

RADIOACTIVE WARFARE

Newspapers have frequently referred to the military use of radioactive materials not produced by the explosion of an A-bomb. They picture an entire city being mysteriously subjected to an invisible death from radioactive particles so small as to be invisible. Through the use of the huge nuclear chain reactors, such as those at Hanford in the state of Washington, large quantities of radioactive materials can be made. Certainly the public is well aware of the radio isotopes being so produced and used by medical men. What is the likelihood that similar materials will be used against us in large quantities?

If an enemy wished to manufacture radioactive material for use as a poison, he would have to make use of a reactor or "pile," as it is commonly called. Fission products are the atom fragments which remain after a Uranium 235 nucleus fissions and since these are of no practical use and are highly radioactive, they might be used directly from the pile. It is a known fact, however, that *most fission products decay or die out rather quickly.* After a few months the radioactivity of the material decreases to a low level as compared with its initial value. As contrasted with the initial flash of radioactivity emitted by an atomic bomb explosion, the radioactivity of the fission products would be very small. It may be argued that if the fission products from a pile are waste, anyway, why not put them to some use? The effective dispersal of a radioactive dust of fission products would require excessively large amounts to be deposited accurately in the target area. The difficulties involved in this

procedure appear to be out of proportion to the results that
might be obtained. Because of decay, such materials could not
be stockpiled, a disadvantage so great as to make radioactive
warfare unlikely. All-in-all, the use of a radioactive agent seems
very impractical and it probably will never be used in actual
warfare except for its psychological effect. Even this will be
relatively unimportant against a thoroughly informed population.

A BASEMENT BURST

Let us now turn our attention to a bomb smuggled into a
city and detonated in the basement of a skyscraper. Certainly
no newspaper reader has missed hearing the term "suitcase
warfare." It has been suggested that foreign agents might in-
filtrate our country and plant bombs in our major cities. These
would be exploded on a predetermined schedule until we had
capitulated or until we had no cities remaining. This possibility
is taken up in the next chapter; at this point we shall deal only
with the probable effects of such a bomb burst, if it were
feasible of execution.

Assume that an atomic bomb is detonated in the basement of
the City Hall at the lower end of Manhattan. As all visitors to
New York know, the City Hall building is situated in a tight
cluster of skyscrapers which rise to a height of about 800 feet
(Fig. 8–1, p. 105). No one knows exactly what would happen if
an atomic bomb were detonated under the conditions described,
but it is evident that the explosion would vent itself by directing
much of its energy in the path of least resistance. Undoubtedly
the building itself would collapse. There would be a considerable earth shock in the vicinity but the actual displacement of
earth to form a crater would not be enormous. A crater some
500 feet in diameter might be expected. Major physical damage
would be confined to an area not more than 1,000 feet in radius,
but the blast wave would undoubtedly cause superficial damage
to buildings at a greater distance.

Skyscrapers have an integral steel skeleton construction to which is attached a facing of masonry. Much of the latter might be expected to be ripped off the buildings and would cascade into the narrow streets of the financial district. The "before" and "after" sketches shown in Fig. 8–2 (pp. 106, 107) illustrate how Wall Street might look from the steps of the Subtreasury Building. Streets thus blocked with debris obviously would be impassable even to the best disaster equipment. Present-day firefighting equipment can not operate over streets strewn with even minor debris. Under such conditions fire, once started, would rage unchecked. The blast damage from this surface burst would be quite localized and would be small compared with that which can be realized by a high air burst. For this reason we believe that the latter type of burst should be considered the most probable form of attack.

Those who expect that the City Hall would be completely vaporized overestimate the power of the bomb. They should remember that at Alamogordo the base of the 100-foot iron tower still remained intact. *Even objects only 100 feet from the center of the bomb explosion were not completely destroyed.* It is also pertinent to recall that the bomb crater at Alamogordo was only 300 feet in diameter and quite shallow. This area, which is still *detectably* radioactive, is by no means *dangerous* today and was a hazard for only a short time.

In a basement burst, primary radiation emitted by the fission process at the time of the explosion would be somewhat restricted, due to the shielding effect of the closely spaced buildings. It would certainly not be comparable to that from an air burst, as at Nagasaki. As the explosion vented itself into the air, it would carry with it most of the radioactive products of the bomb, although residual radioactivity at the bomb site would remain for some time. The neutron flash could be expected to induce some activity in surrounding structures but this would not be a major hazard.

AN AIR BURST OVER MANHATTAN

As Fig. 8–1 illustrates so graphically, Manhattan has two dense clumps of skyscrapers, one in the financial district at the tip of the island and the other just east of Times Square. Here each day the subways, buses, and trains disgorge some three million people who work in Manhattan. In such a tiny space there would not be sufficient room unless people were stacked one on top of another and this is virtually what is done in a city of skyscraper construction. Prior to the atomic bomb this seemed a reasonable procedure, although it did entail some difficulties in transportation, water supply, and housing.

Let us consider what an atomic bomb would do to midtown Manhattan if it were burst over the intersection of 42nd Street and 5th Avenue. We shall explode our hypothetical bomb about a thousand feet above the street, or 200 feet below the tip of the Empire State Building. We must consider three effects of the bomb—the flash of heat, the flash of penetrating radiation, and the blast wave. In a city like New York, especially in the midtown area, the heat flash would not be too important, for more fires would probably start from secondary origin than from direct ignition. Most significant to the population would be the instantaneous burst of gamma rays that would flash out from the bomb. We believe that this radiation would give a lethal dose to a person in the open at a distance of slightly less than one mile. Fig. 8–3 (p. 83) is a pictorial map of the area. On it the Empire State Building is slightly over 2,000 feet from the site of the explosion. People in this building would receive a dose of gamma rays about 15 times the lethal amount. No other buildings would shield this colossus from the direct flash of radiation and the shielding effect of its walls would be very slight. The Empire State Building is remarkable for its light construction; in addition it has a large window area which would freely admit the radiation. At this distance from the burst, a person inside the structure would have to be shielded

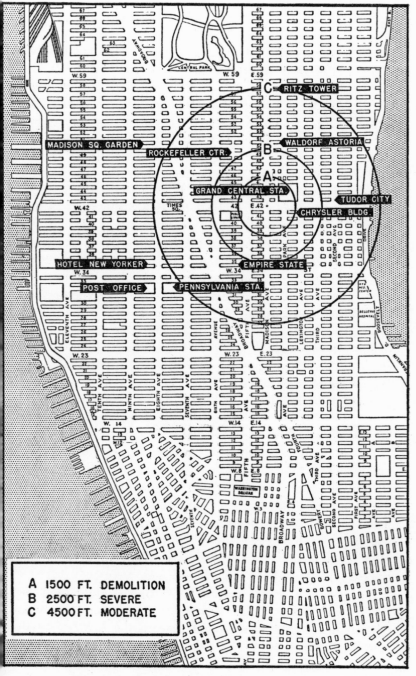

A 1500 FT. DEMOLITION
B 2500 FT. SEVERE
C 4500 FT. MODERATE

Fig. 8–3 Zones of damage from an air burst.

83

on all sides by about 20 inches of concrete in order to survive.
This is little consolation, for the blast effect on the building
would also be spectacular. The building would not be toppled
by the blast wave because the panel type walls would blow off
first, leaving a skeletal framework. People in the upper stories
would be blown right out of the building.

Strangely enough, buildings closer to the center of the blast
probably would suffer less damage than the Empire State
Building because of shielding effects and because the blast wave
would not hit them directly from the side. Structures like Radio
City and the Chrysler Building would be hard hit and in them
the loss of life would be exceedingly high. These skyscrapers
tower over 800 feet skyward and one of them may contain as
many as 30,000 people. The city would have to receive an
alert at least an hour before the attack if these structures were
to be evacuated and the people safely housed in the subways
or other shelters. *Directly under the center of the blast, people
in the subways would be unaffected either by the blast or by
the radiation. They would be perfectly safe.* People farther from
the center of the blast would also be safe if they were in the
lower floors of buildings shielded from the flash of radiation.

SKYSCRAPERS AS TARGETS

It is difficult to estimate the number of people likely to be
killed by this hypothetical explosion. On the assumption that
there was no adequate alert and no effective evacuation, our
estimates show that about 200,000 people would die and
250,000 more would be injured. These figures are somewhat
conservative; they could run higher, but if there were an early
alert and people followed a well worked out disaster plan,
the casualties would be sharply reduced.

A glance at a photograph of Manhattan at night (Fig. 8–4,
p. 108) shows us why these figures are so high. Note the myriad
of windows shining in the night. Here is the Achilles' heel of
New York. For these very windows that admit light also offer

no barrier to the primary radiation from the bomb. They make skyscrapers into virtual "radiation cells" in which people would be irradiated like bees in a hive. By their very height and limited means of egress skyscrapers prevent people from fleeing in time of peril. They can not be made strong enough to support sufficient masonry for adequate protection against radiation.

The lesson is more than clear. It is not necessary to cite further details about Manhattan. *Such cities are cities of the past.* In an Atomic Age no nation can afford to present such a perfect target to an enemy. This will not be good news to property owners on the fabulous island but perhaps it is better to have property values change gradually over a period of years than to have the change come abruptly when the first bomb drops.

New York is not the only city that presents such an acme of vulnerability. Chicago's Loop district ranks a close second. Here it was that the first skyscraper was born. Within the compact area of a relatively few blocks (Fig. 8–5, p. 109) much of Chicago's business is concentrated. Here are the big hotels, department stores, and business houses. A single bomb detonated over the Civic Opera House would do an effective job of knocking out the Loop. The Merchandise Mart, across the river, would be hard hit by the blast and its thousands of denizens would suffer the same fate as those in the Empire State Building. Chicago, being further inland than New York, might have the advantage of an earlier alert and might therefore suffer fewer casualties.

Chicago is situated along the shores of Lake Michigan and except for a strip of beautiful parkway it touches the lakefront for many miles. Lake Michigan is a large body of water and one might assume that a water burst here (certainly not from a tramp steamer, but from an aerial bomb) could be effective. But Chicago, like so many other American cities, is fortunate. *There is water but it is not very deep.* In fact, close in to shore

Lake Michigan is quite shallow; its depth is only 15 to 18 feet directly in front of the Loop and increases to 32 feet three miles from shore. But in common with all metropolitan areas, Chicago's Loop is vulnerable to an air burst. It is this type of attack that is most destructive and against which our cities should be defended.

A Chicago minus its Loop would be a giant without a heart. True, there are other more critical targets, the destruction of which would have a more immediate effect upon our war-making capacity, but in the long run the loss of Chicago would be a serious blow to our national economy. The effect upon the industrialized Midwest would be to spread paralysis to all the interlinked industries which are dependent upon the industrial output of this great city. The disruption of communications and transportation would be severe. Elimination of key individuals in civic life, commerce, finance, and industry would add to the chaos. All of these effects would be magnified because of the overconcentration of men and machines in a single city.

The author takes this opportunity to express his appreciation for permission to use the photographs in the following pages.

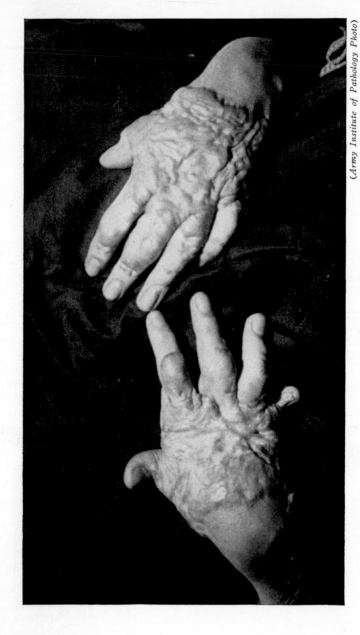

Fig. 2-1 A burn survivor of an incendiary raid on Tokyo. Note the crippling effect of the burns and the heavy keloids.

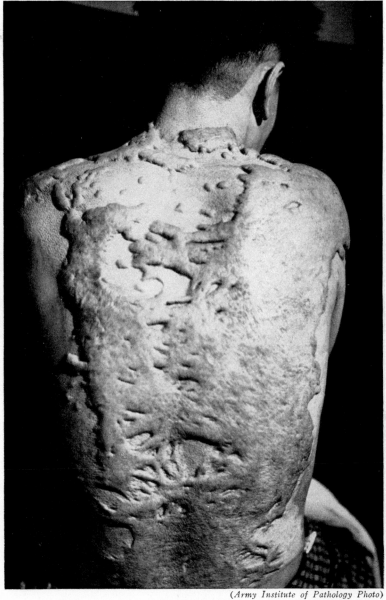

Fig. 2–2 Heavy keloid formation in a survivor of the Nagasaki
atomic attack.

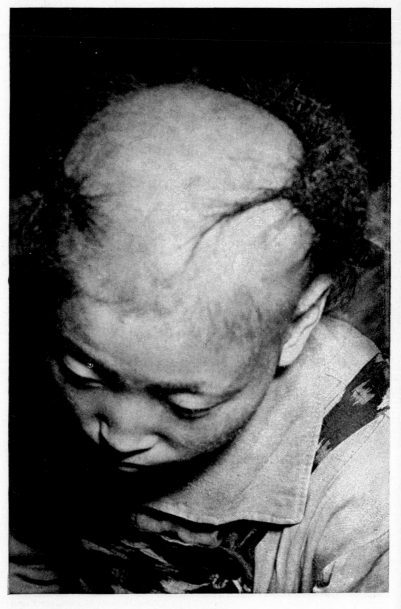

Fig. 2–3 Epilation resulting from the absorption of penetrating radiation.

90

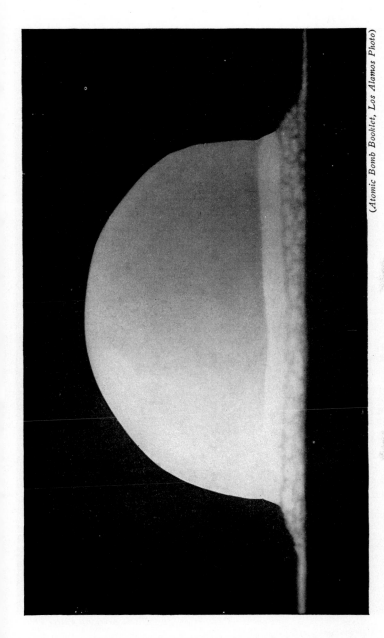

Fig. 3–1   The Alamogordo fireball.

Fig. 3–2 Surface scorching at about one mile from an air burst bomb. Note the shadows cast by the steel members on the undamaged tank.

Fig. 3–3 The mushroom cloud almost completely formed (Bikini).

(*USAFC Photo*)

Fig. 3–4 Hereford cattle which were exposed to fall-out. The white hair on the back is a result of the action of nuclear radiation.

Fig. 4-1   The TEST BAKER water column. The base surge is just starting to form.

(U. S. Army Air Forces Photo)

Fig. 4-2   The start of the base surge.

Fig. 5–1   Safety monitors at Bikini.

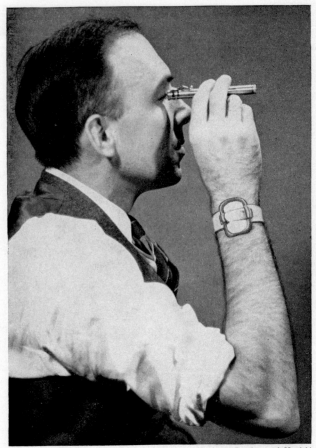

Fig. 5–2 The use of personnel protection instruments. Note the film badge worn on the wrist.

Fig. 6–3 Effects of saturation bombing at Wesel, Germany.

Fig. 6-4 (a) Bomb damage in Ulm, Germany.

Fig. 6–4 (b) Bomb damage in Nuremberg, Germany.

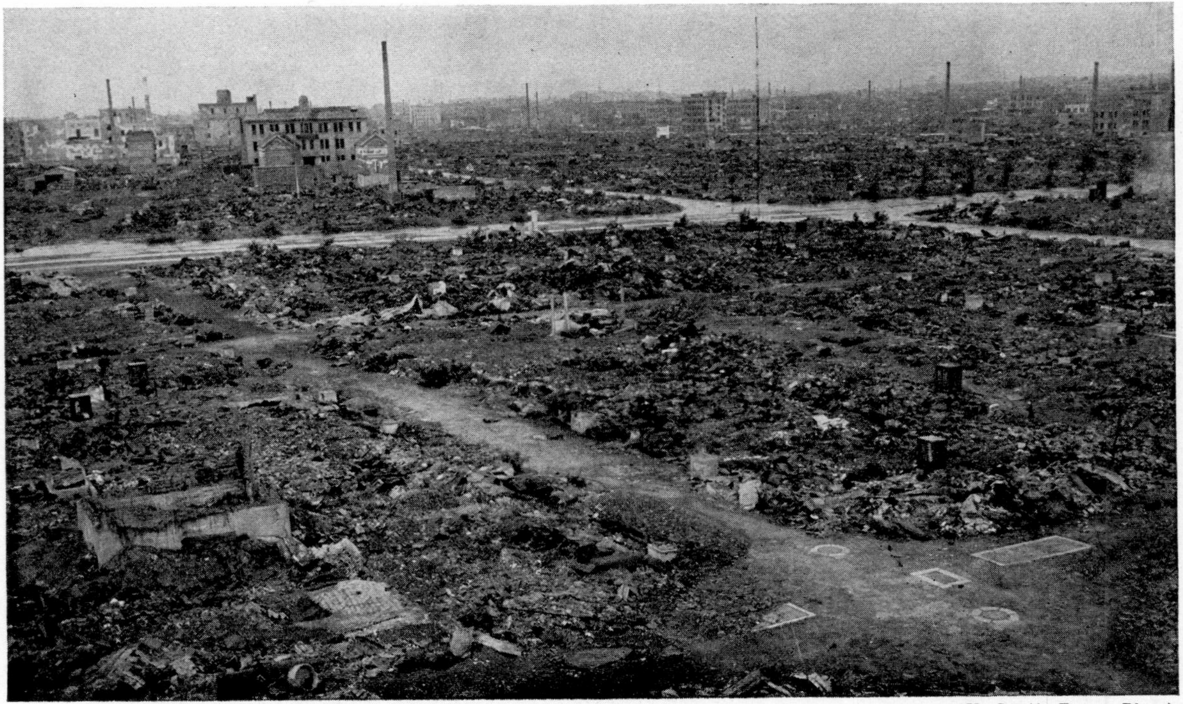

Fig. 7-2 The ruins of Tokyo after an incendiary raid.

102

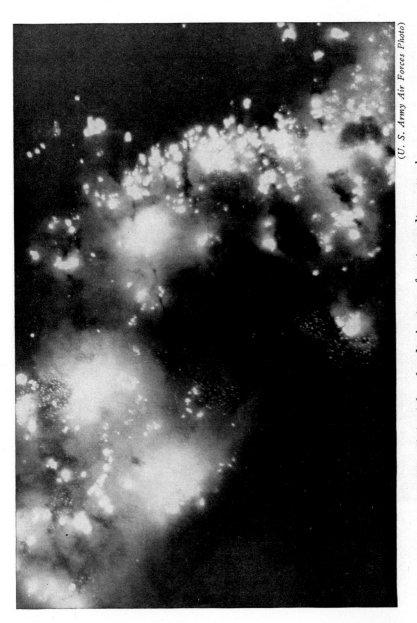

Fig. 7-4 A bombardier's view of an incendiary attack.

1000'

Fig. 7–5 Atomic bomb damage at Hiroshima.

Fig. 8–1   Aerial view of Manhattan.

Fig. 8–2 (a)   Wall Street—"before."

Fig. 8-2 (b) Wall Street—"after."

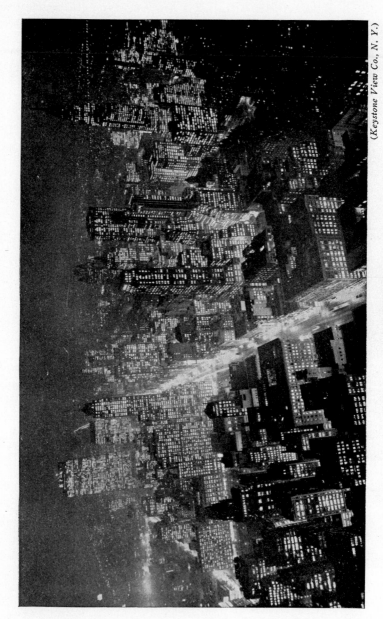

Fig. 8-4 Manhattan at night.

Fig. 8–5   Chicago's Loop viewed from the lakefront.

(*U. S. Air Forces Photo*)

Fig. 9–1 A V–2 poised for launching at White Sands Proving
Grounds, N. M.

Fig. 9–3   A B–36 in flight.

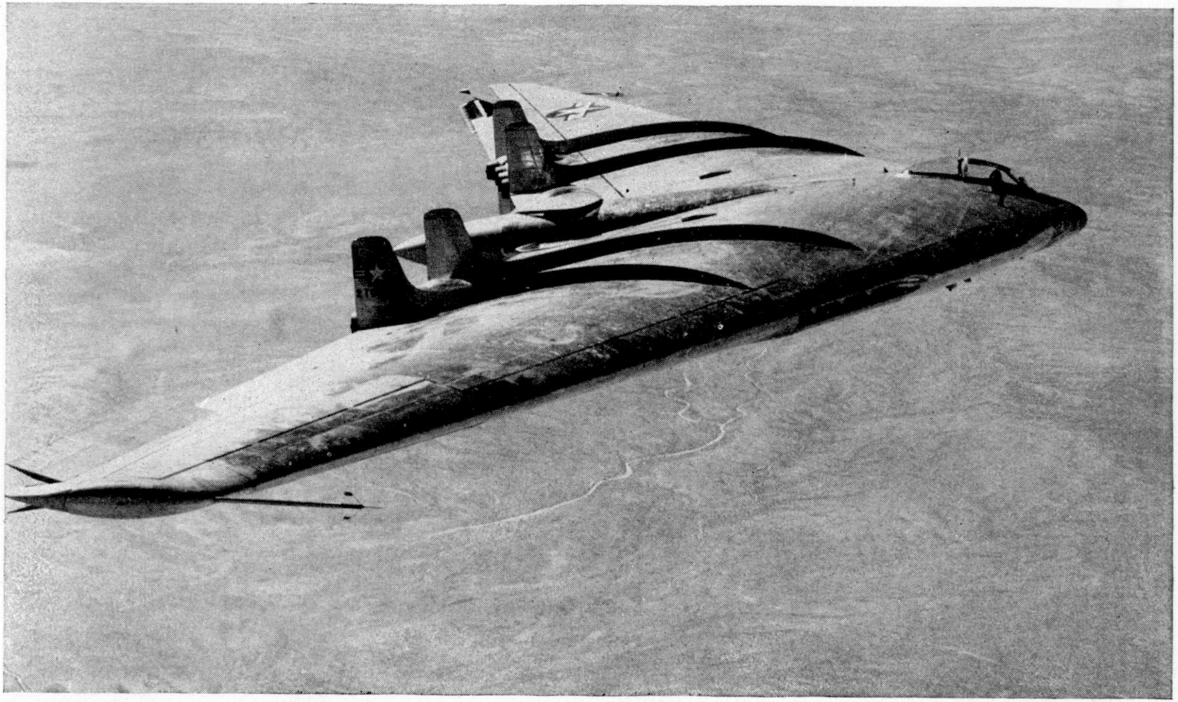

Fig. 9–4   A flying wing jet bomber.

Fig. 9–5   An artist's conception of the new supercarrier.

Fig. 10–2   The Navy's new XF7U–1 jet interceptor.

Fig. 11-1   The business district of Houston, Texas.

Fig. 11–3 Part of the atomic energy installation at Hanford.

Fig. 11–4 One of the plants at Oak Ridge.

Fig. 11–5   A bombardier's view of the Pentagon.

Chapter 9
THE DELIVERY PROBLEM

"The atomic bomb is only useful when it is delivered to the target, and in too many cases this may be an impossible task."

—Admiral R. A. Ofstie, u.s.n.

It is one thing to have a stock pile of bombs and quite another thing to deliver these weapons to their targets. Nor has this problem been greatly eased by the advent of the atomic bomb. Public statements suggest that only a B–29 or its equivalent is capable of transporting the A-bomb. Whatever the size or complexity may be, it is certain that it is not a pocket-sized object which an enemy agent may conceal on his person.

Shortly after the end of World War II, some envisaged a United States open to infiltration by enemy agents equipped with atomic bombs. These bombs would be planted in our cities and exploded at an opportune time. Or, they pointed out, in time of peace a tramp steamer might enter an American harbor and detonate an atomic bomb there. Let us make clear that the atomic bomb has no unique identification which allows its detection either when planted in a city or stored in the hold of a cargo ship. In fact, Dr. Oppenheimer stated in a Congressional hearing that he thought the most important tool (for detection) would be a screwdriver, to open all crates for inspection. Obviously it would not be feasible to board each vessel and conduct a search thorough enough to find an A-bomb. It would completely disrupt our maritime commerce. This being the case, are we to live in perpetual fear of such subversive activities? It seems not. It appears that both a surface and an underwater burst are poor selections for American targets. Surface shots do only limited damage and underwater detonations would probably be of nuisance value only. But there are even more compelling arguments which mitigate the use of the atomic bomb in covert operations.

What would an enemy high command do if a proposal were made to them that a number, say twenty, atomic bombs be allocated to fifth columnists for placement in American cities? First, such a proposal probably would be turned down if the stock pile were not many times larger than twenty bombs. Second, if any of the twenty bombs were discovered en route or at their destination, the initiative would immediately pass to the United States. Two vital pieces of information would then be ours—intelligence as to enemy intention and, more important, information about enemy capability. Any country finding atomic bombs of foreign manufacture concealed within its border would not long hesitate to launch an offensive against the suspect nation. We are inclined to believe that in the foreseeable future the identity of the suspect nation would not be in doubt.

The foregoing arguments lead to the conclusion that any nation seeking to attack the United States with atomic bombs will employ aerial delivery. This conclusion is further substantiated by the fact that an air burst would produce the most destructive results against the targets we present. Let us now examine some of the problems connected with the delivery of atomic weapons by air.

GUIDED MISSILES

Any Englishman can testify to the terror of a V–2 attack. From the security of bases across the Channel, Germany launched its huge missile into the air (Fig. 9–1, p. 110). Fourteen tons of rocket surged forward into the air, propelled by a jet exhaust. In a matter of a few seconds after the alcohol and liquid oxygen were ignited the missile rose from its platform and soared skyward, gradually gaining speed. A minute later the jet engine was cut off and, controlled by internal guidance, the missile arched towards its target some 200 miles away. Still climbing, the V–2 rose to an altitude of almost sixty miles and then descended in its parabolic trajectory. Five minutes after launching, the V–2 crashed on England and if all went well it hit somewhere within four miles of its aiming point. The lack of accuracy was compensated for by the sprawling nature of the target—the city of London. In this way, some 2,000 V–2s crossed the Channel and somewhat more than half of these hit in the vicinity of London. Because the V–2s approached the target with a speed of more than 1,000 miles per hour, they could not be intercepted. *The only defense consisted of seizing control of the launching areas.*

Research and development involved in the evolution of the V–2 cost the Germans a tremendous outlay of men, material, and effort. The Peenemünde establishment, where the V–2 was developed, is said to have cost more than $120,000,000. As an offensive weapon the V–2 was ineffective, for its warhead consisted of but one ton of high explosive. Had the Germans diverted their effort to the development of short-range ground-to-air missiles for defense instead of squandering on the V–2, the results might have been disastrous to the Allied air fleets over Germany. As it was, the V–2 and its companion piece the V–1 (or robot bomb) achieved technical excellence but lacked effectiveness as military weapons.

With typical German persistence, the V–2 was designed and repeatedly redesigned until the final weapon attained a high degree of perfection. But had the Germans not been favored with launching platforms just across the Channel, they might have been forced to change their plans for employment of the V–2. Many V–2s have been fired since the war's end at the White Sands Proving Grounds in New Mexico but none has given promise of travelling more than 300 miles.

Newspapers have reported that Germany had an A–10 missile under development for traversing the Atlantic Ocean. *It is a singularly long jump to proceed from the V–2, with its limited range, to a missile capable of travelling thousands of miles.* Such transoceanic missiles, when developed, will be extremely large and costly vehicles. How much of a nation's economy can be devoted to the production of such huge items of military hardware will be a serious consideration. Anyone who has had experience in the rocket field knows that the construction of long-range missiles involves all of the complexity of manufacture usually associated with aircraft assembly; they are not cheap. This development is probably far in the future, and we need not pursue the subject of intercontinental rocketry further here. No one familiar with the progress of air technology has any doubt that a war tomorrow or ten years from now will be fought with the latest models of conventional aircraft. In such a war, the long-range delivery vehicles will be planes powered by present-day engines or by jet propulsion.

LONG-RANGE BOMBERS

Before the development of the atomic bomb, aircraft were designed to carry high-explosive bombs and incendiaries. The tendency was to increase the size of the bomb bay to carry larger and larger payloads. For this increased bomb-carrying capacity it was necessary to build a proportionately larger airframe. Then it was realized that a long-range aircraft could not depend entirely upon fighters for its protection. As a result, the heavy bombardment craft were armored and equipped with multiple gun turrets. The B–17, pitted against speedy

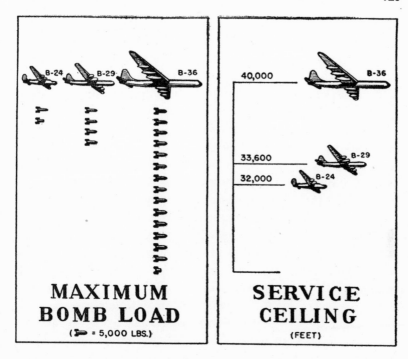

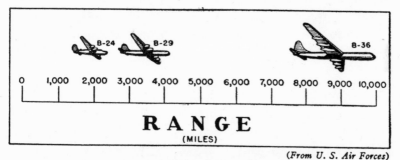

(From U. S. Air Forces)

Fig. 9–2   Trends in bomber development.

German interceptors, was forced to don a mantle of increased firepower so that it finally resembled a fortress bristling with guns. From the B–17 there evolved the Superfortress, or the B–29, with its complex defensive armament. Another trend in the evolution of the heavy bomber was the development of high-altitude aircraft. Antiaircraft guns often proved extremely effective during the past war in keeping bombers up at such a high altitude that bombing was less accurate. At very high altitude, flak became less of a problem simply because of technical difficulties inherent in antiaircraft fire. It is probable that ground-to-air guided missiles will substitute for the antiaircraft batteries to harass high-flying bombers. The three trends in bomber development—increased bomb load (and plane size), service ceiling, and range are graphically displayed in Fig. 9–2.

Fig. 9–3 (p. 111) shows the B–36 which, because of its tremendous size and complexity, required over 6½ years in the design and development stage. It was designed prior to knowledge of the atomic bomb and consequently called for a very large bomb load. A word of explanation should be made with respect to the information given in Fig. 9–2. The range and bomb load of a long-range aircraft are intimately associated. The longer the range, the lighter the bomb load. For a short haul, the B–36 is capable of carrying 36 tons of bombs in its four bomb bays but for maximum range it has a five-ton bomb limit. Yet this huge plane weighs more than 150 tons. Some facts about the B–36 as constructed by the Consolidated Vultee Aircraft Corp. are summarized below:

Gross weight		163 tons
Length		163 feet
Wingspan		230 feet
Height		46 feet
Maximum bomb load		36 tons (2 Grand Slam bombs)
Armament	16	20 mm cannons
	1	37 mm cannon
(optional)	1	F–85 parasite jet fighter
Fuel capacity		21,000 gallons (2½ tank cars)
Power plant	6	3500 hp engines
Average speed		330 mph at 37,000 ft.
Crew		15 men

The fundamental obstacle to overcome in the development of a long-range bomber is the attainment of high speed and long range in one and the same aircraft. The bomber must have high speed so that it is not easily intercepted; high speed means greater fuel consumption; more fuel necessitates added weight in the airframe; added weight means still greater fuel consumption; and so it goes in a vicious circle. The result is something of a compromise but it does end up with a very heavy craft which is none too fast over the target.

Arming a heavy bomber with defensive equipment is done only at the sacrifice of speed and range. Experience of the past war showed that bombers were unable to defend themselves against highly maneuverable interceptors. In fact, it was better to leave guns off the bomber and fly higher and faster. This procedure may have had a momentary adverse psychological effect on the crew, but in the long run it was successful, for fewer bomber losses were sustained.

JET-PROPELLED BOMBERS

During the past few years, the introduction of jet propulsion has brought forth radically new designs in high-speed aircraft. Speeds of 600 mph and more are now commonplace. Multiple jets, such as the "flying wing" or YB–49 shown in Fig. 9–4 (p. 112) propel even heavy bombers at very high speed. Unfortunately, jet engines are "fuel eaters" and as yet have not been developed for use in very long-range aircraft. Some models weigh 60 tons and have a range shorter than from Chicago to San Francisco. It is doubtful that the fuel-hungry jets can soon be weaned sufficiently to give them a range comparable to that of the B–36. For some time to come jet bombers must be classed as vehicles of limited range. This is deplorable, for jets have over-the-target speeds which render them much less vulnerable than the lumbering B–36.

True dyed-in-the-wool air enthusiasts are insistent that air power be self-sufficient and not dependent upon bases close to the enemy. They would view with some disdain strategic bombing that could only be carried on from bases 1500 or 2000 miles from the target. Major de Seversky typifies the extremists who define strategic bombing as that which is based in the United States or nearby. Advocates of long-range bombing point out that we may be helpless to retaliate against an enemy if we are deprived of our advance bases and do not possess aircraft like the B–36. Others argue that we must hold the advance bases and must secure them at all costs.

Here is where the Navy enters the argument, for it is obvious that advance overseas bases must be supported by a naval force. The Navy aggressively insists that it can not only support advance land bases but it can send aircraft carriers to within jet range of the target and to this end the Navy Department has authorized construction of the much discussed supercarrier shown as an artist's conception in Fig. 9–5 (p. 113). This 1090-foot carrier would displace 65,000 tons and presumably would cost more than 200 million dollars, illustrating once again the mounting cost of a delivery vehicle for the atomic bomb in the present stage of our technology. The controversy between the Air Force and the Navy as to who will deliver the A-bombs is a lively one and has many ramifications, the discussion of which would take us far afield. We would have to consider many technical factors, not the least of which is the vulnerability of a large carrier to air and submarine attack.

ATOMIC PROPULSION

Both in the case of missiles and manned aircraft, the weight of the fuel which must be carried is a limiting design criterion. Is there a way out of this dilemma, which so severely limits the usefulness of chemical fuels? Offhand it would seem that nuclear energy offers the ideal solution to the aircraft fuel problem, for uranium liberates millions of times more power than chemical fuel. However, there are many technical difficulties to be overcome before a nuclear power plant can be adapted to aircraft propulsion. Some of these are so formidable that it is even doubtful that a nuclear propulsion plant can be made light enough to be carried in a craft of the B–36 size. Furthermore, any nuclear power reactor produces a very large amount of penetrating radiation and will require heavy shielding if the plane is to be maintained and operated. Current estimates place the minimum weight of the shield required for this purpose at many tons.

There are many other technical difficulties to be faced. An orderly approach to the problem would depend upon the development of a stationary nuclear power plant. Even here the development is so difficult that the Atomic Energy Commission Semiannual Report states that it will take ". . . from 8 to 10 years to overcome the technical difficulties and have a useful, practical demonstration plant in operation." The jump from this stationary nuclear power plant to an airborne unit will be another big one.

Apparently, then, nuclear-propelled aircraft are at least 15 years in the future and fall beyond the time area encompassed by this book. This time estimate is concurred in by qualified scientists. During this period we may confidently expect the performance of non-nuclear powered aircraft to improve and increasing range probably will be achieved with jet propulsion, but for five years or more truly long-range aircraft will be powered by reciprocating engines. In other words, our striking force will consist of B–50s (improved version of the B–29) and B–36s. The B–36 has had its ups and downs in the Air Force. It has been in favor one day and out of favor the next. Too often the problem of the usefulness of the B–36 has been oversimplified by assuming that it could be easily shot down by a jet interceptor. To bring down the B–36, the interceptor must be in the air near it and if an inadequate alert is given, this may not be possible. As we shall see in the next chapter, *the alert is all important in any defense scheme.*

Inherent in our discussion has been the assumption that the bombers would fly a round trip. We must not overlook the fact

that an enemy nation might send one-way missions aimed at the
United States, leaving the bomber crews to take care of themselves after the bomb release. It would be folly to assume that
only the Japanese are of the temperament to undertake suicide
missions. Such tactics would enable the enemy to use short-
range planes for long-range missions and thus more fully insure
delivery of bombs to their targets.

Chapter 10

ACTIVE DEFENSE

"There are, and there will be, no specific counter-measures to atomic weapons."

—J. ROBERT OPPENHEIMER

Many people have voiced the opinion that there is no defense against the atomic bomb. Just why anyone would expect that a specific defense would be found is a curious question. Certainly no one expects a defense against TNT. Perhaps it was the magic of the word "atomic" which misled the layman. Actually, the problem of defense against an atomic bomb is technically the same as defense against any other type of bomb. There is no mysterious ray or beam which can be used to prevent an atomic bomb from exploding or to cause it to explode prematurely. But we must stress the point that *active defense,* which consists of intercepting the bomb en route, must be more foolproof than defense against ordinary high-explosive bombs. One atomic bomb packs a big wallop in a small package and we simply can not afford to let an appreciable number slip through the defense ring. The task of establishing a means of alerting our defense system is itself truly gigantic. When the problem of intercepting enemy bombers is added, the difficulties become tremendous. In fact, *the active defenses,* such as fighter planes and guided missiles, may be quite incapable of intercepting more than about 20 percent of the invading force. This is merely a restatement of the tenet that the power of the offense surpasses that of the defense.

Because so many bombers may be able to penetrate our defense net, it is most important that we consider every possible measure which may reduce the effectiveness of the bombs that are delivered. We believe that there are measures which can be effective if they are properly planned and carried out. For the present, we shall discuss active defenses against the delivery of atomic weapons.

Under the head of active defense, two things come immediately to mind: the use of special agents to discover the surreptitious activities of the enemy and the employment of physical devices, such as fighter planes and missiles, to intercept the enemy bombers. To these we add a third: *the destruction of the enemy's long-range bombers and bomber bases.* The latter is really a counterpart of the interception phase of defense; it is merely an extension of interception to the time before the bombers take off from their home air fields. An enemy shorn of his long-range bombers would not be able to deliver his atomic bombs.

Finally, we must consider retaliation. Not that this is really a defensive measure, for it is not, except only in the sense that it is meant to be a means of bringing the enemy to terms.

INTELLIGENCE INTERCEPTION

Two avenues of approach for enemy agents in the surreptitious delivery of atomic weapons have already been touched upon: a bomb might be hidden aboard a tramp steamer and detonated in a United States port or it might be smuggled into an American city and detonated at basement or street level.

We have already shown that neither of these techniques

would produce very effective results. An even more compelling reason to avoid surreptitious delivery is that the risk of discovery of the bombs prior to A-day would be great. If just one bomb of foreign origin is uncovered, the aggressor loses his initiative—and this, above all else, he will prize in an atomic war. It is reasonable to assume that the United States would be at war within a few hours after the discovery of an atomic bomb planted in one of its cities. Some people have advanced the view that we might be in doubt as to the identity of the aggressor and end up in a diplomatic snarl of charges and countercharges wherein we would lose the initiative. Perhaps such a condition might obtain in the very distant future, but not within the next 15 years. During that time few countries besides the United States can conceivably have the atomic bomb and be classed as aggressors.

Intelligence agents will not be able to detect the presence of atomic bombs by means of Geiger counters or by other special apparatus. As Dr. Oppenheimer has so neatly put it, the best detection device is a screwdriver! He further stated before a Congressional Committee that ". . . the active material in any designs (of atomic bombs) we have been concerned with is like a small diamond in an enormous wad of cotton wool." *There are and there will be no instruments capable of detecting the presence of atomic bombs.* Our agents must use conventional intelligence methods to ferret out any covert atomic bomb infiltration into the United States. It is to be hoped that we will soon begin to be more than just aware of the *need* for adequate intelligence agencies and that we will actually undertake intelligence operations on a scale and in a manner consistent with the magnitude of the problem.

It will be of great importance for our intelligence forces to know the capabilities of the enemy in the field of atomic weapons. To know merely that a foreign nation has tested one atomic bomb will not mean much except to add a single entry in our intelligence book. Much more significant will be knowl-

edge about the kind and quantities of atomic bombs being
produced.

Recollection of the Pearl Harbor disaster brings keenly to
mind the truth that *intelligence must be used if it is to be
effective*. The time between learning something and doing
something about it in the atomic age must be short. It is certainly conceivable that failure to act quickly upon vital intelligence data may mean disaster to a portion of our populace.
This is more than a mechanical problem of accumulating information with radar or detection equipment. It is a problem of
being on the alert 24 hours of the day, every day of the year.

ALERTING THE DEFENSE

For any defense system to be effective it must be alerted. In
the days of highspeed aircraft, the problem of detecting the
presence of an invading force is far from solved. World War II
saw the development of radar and its use to detect enemy aircraft. However, the conditions of the last war were different
from those we face today. Today planes fly higher and faster.
Only a few planes are needed for an atomic mission. Furthermore, the areas to be defended are immense. The United States
and its approaches by air only faintly resemble those of Germany. The problem of detecting enemy aircraft approaching
the United States is a formidable one. We have said that space
is our ally, but when it comes to setting up a system of detection,
such as a radar "picket fence," around our borders, it works
against us. It will take a huge number of radar posts, a multitude of technicians to man them, and constant vigilance to
maintain such a system. Even then it may not guarantee successful detection. A radar net is like a dike; one hole may bring
disaster.

As we shall see in the next chapter, the heart of United States
production capacity and its concentrated centers of population
lie in a relatively small area in the northeast. To the north there
is sparsely populated Canada and to the east there is the

Atlantic Ocean. If we tried to throw a complete radar cordon around this area, we would have to maintain a constant sea patrol of radar picket ships. This assignment would be both difficult and costly.

Cities farther from the heart of the nation and away from the coasts might enjoy a fuller measure of security because the alert would be more adequate, but enemy bombers might successfully penetrate far into the interior if the arctic route were used. We might detect them, but interception would be another story.

An invading force might well take advantage of bad weather or might conduct night raids to minimize bomber losses, but if the people in metropolitan areas were the targets the raids would have to be conducted as daylight operations to produce the greatest number of casualties. This is a favorable circumstance from the standpoint of defense, for the probability of detection and interception is increased.

DEFENSE OPERATIONS

Just as soon as a given section of the country is alerted to the peril of an enemy attack, areas within that section would be immediately alerted and defenses would be activated. This is shown schematically in Fig. 10–1. The control organization, upon receipt of the initial alert, activates its special devices operations center, at the same time sending aloft its complement of jet fighter planes to seek out the enemy at a distance from the target. Guided missiles are used as interceptory devices near the target area to counter planes which get through the fighter array. Throughout the attack the special devices center, operating all types of locating equipment, automatically advises the guided missiles and antiaircraft units of the exact location of each enemy bomber.

If only one or two bombers appeared on the scene, the interception problem would be somewhat simpler for the defending forces. But no enemy would entrust a lone bomber with an atomic bomb. Instead, a number of decoy bombers would undoubtedly accompany it and these could later be used for missions using incendiaries, high explosives, or even propaganda pamphlets.

A defense operation center is a highly complex organization into which information about the location and course of the

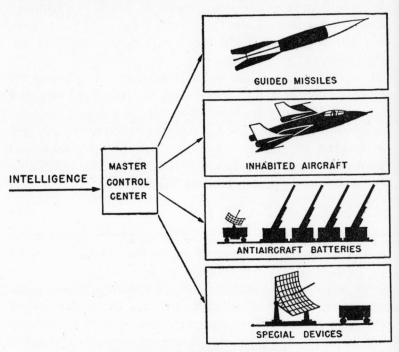

Fig. 10-1 Air defense systems.

enemy planes feeds continuously. From the center, information and direction go out to three types of interception devices. First line action goes to the fighter planes, for these have greatest flexibility in deployment and action in the earliest phase of the alert. Furthermore, they are able to strike at the invading force long before it gets over the target, provided they are alerted in time. The next line of defense action goes to the guided missiles unit. While these have less flexibility than the fighters, in that they must be launched from locations near the target, they do have distinct advantages. The number of missiles units that can be allocated to the defense of any installation is limited by the fact that it would be economically impossible to set up a complete ring of such units at any great distance from every target. Yet if high-speed, high-flying bombers are employed, the bomb may be released 15 miles from the target. Obviously, the bomber would have to be intercepted prior to bomb release, for the chance of hitting the bomb itself in flight would be negligible. Against high altitude planes, antiaircraft batteries would probably be quite ineffective even if proximity-fused shells were used.

We emphasize again that early detection of enemy bombers is all-important. *Defenses are worthless unless they are alerted.* Once alerted, the defenses depend upon the effectiveness of the weapons which are available. At the end of the last war, the Germans had devised some exceedingly deadly interception devices and had they been able to achieve quantity production, the air over Germany would have been very unhealthy for our bombers.

DEFENSIVE AIR WEAPONS

Not only did the Germans develop high-speed jet interceptors that could fly circles around bombers, but they had perfected aerial rockets which could be fired from underwing locations. They had developed ground-to-air missiles which would have been a serious menace to air operations had they been available in quantity. Fortunately, they did not develop a proximity fuse device; this would have dealt a crippling blow to our bomber activity.

Today the United States has many new types of jet planes capable of speeds greater than 600 miles per hour. Some of these, such as the Navy's XF7U-1, shown in Fig. 10-2 (p. 114) resemble rockets more than they do aircraft.

The offensive-defensive problem is too often oversimplified by the following type of argument. If a jet interceptor is matched against a heavy bombardment type craft, the jet fighter will possess the advantage of speed and maneuverability; hence it will be able to bring the bomber down in flames. The fighter probably does have the edge in this battle, but the trick is to get the fighter up off the ground to intercept the bomber. Too often it may happen that the fighters will be still on the runways when the bombers are on their bomb runs. Bad weather and night operations will also limit the effectiveness of fighter interception.

In the realm of guided missiles, much improvement can be expected in the future. Perhaps devices will be developed that unerringly guide the missile towards an invading aircraft and explode it inside the lethal range of the bomber. Such gadgets would be called "homing" devices and might operate on the principle that sensitive instruments would detect heat from the enemy plane and use this as a marker. Other possibilities exist and these will no doubt be thoroughly investigated by our defense establishment. However, we do not expect a magic type of ray to be developed that will mysteriously disable an invading bomber or blast it from the sky. Nor do we expect that atomic bombs will be used as defensive weapons in an air attack.

Even granting that exceedingly effective interception devices are developed, there still remains the fact that they must be available in quantity and they must be used to be effective. It seems highly probable that a large percentage of enemy bombers will get through to their targets. Since this is the case, it is clear that high priority should be assigned the task of destroying the enemy's striking force while it is still on the ground.

RETALIATION

The age-old pattern of war has been a pitting of the offense against the defense. In conformity with the weapons of the offense, man sought security by molding appropriate defenses. Witness the development of the high-walled fortresses in medieval times, or recall that Ch'in Shih Huang Ti, the first Emperor of China, constructed the huge system of fortifications known as the Great Wall. But even the Great Wall, built before the birth of Christ, proved inadequate before the Mongol hordes under Genghis Khan. For every time the defense stiffened, new techniques were invented to sharpen the power of the offense. In more modern times, the French Maginot line is typical of a system of defense made obsolete by blitzkrieg techniques.

So often have people been awakened from their complacent reliance upon a defense by innovations peculiar to the offense, that the maxim "the best defense is a good offense" has gained wide acceptance. That this is the currently accepted view is indicated by the following quotation from the preface to the report of the Congressional group on National Aviation Policy. "The only 'defense' will be swift and more devastating retaliatory attack."

Can we be sure that this policy of quick retaliation is really valid in the Atomic Age? For if we are to fully implement the Air Force Four-Year Plan (commonly called the 70-group plan) we must believe that the power of retaliation is supreme. If we envisage a time in the future when another nation might have atomic weapons and high-speed aircraft in quantities necessary for delivery we must ask ourselves how this retaliatory effort will induce the enemy to quit the war. Obviously, we must inflict terrific punishment upon the enemy in a short time, so that the will to resist is weakened. How will this be done? We might strike at the enemy's cities and centers of industry. Most nations have concentrated the bulk of their population in a few hundred cities, and this might render feasible the knocking out of a country merely by depleting the population. In fact, it has been estimated that no nation which loses 10% of its population in a war can survive. But we feel that this would not qualify as defense, even if finally successful in causing a cessation of hostilities. In terms of defense, the retaliation would have to prevent further attacks from being launched upon our home territory. It is very difficult to see how retaliatory attacks, even with atomic bombs, could deprive the enemy of its bases, for these are not particularly vulnerable to attack, especially if dispersed. Hitting at plants that *were* producing A-bombs would make little sense; you would have to strike at the places where the bombs are stored. For example, it would make little sense for an enemy to strike at our plants at Oak Ridge, for the bombs we have already produced are the targets to be hit, not the plants capable of producing more A-bombs. Similarly, striking at the aircraft industry would seem futile, for the enemy would not have launched a war without accumulating a sufficient number of bombers for the initial blitz.

A good offense constitutes the best defense *only if it is successful in preventing the enemy from delivering a significant number of atomic bombs to our home targets.* Because atomic bombs give an enemy the capability to inflict heavy damage in a short time interval, the concept of a good offense as the best defense is changed. Yet one can search through most official public documents on the subject of air power and fail to find even an inkling that this is true. No doubt it was true in pre-atomic times when General Douhet wrote, "Viewed in its true light, aerial warfare admits of no defense, only offense. We must therefore resign ourselves to the offensives the enemy inflicts upon us, while striving to put all our resources to work to inflict even heavier ones upon him." Thus did the air prophet spell out the words which now highlight the current inconsistency of air power.

Chapter 11
TARGET: U.S.A.

"The Atomic Bomb does not give us automatic immunity, as some people would like to believe, nor does its mere possession guarantee victory should war come."

—JAMES FORRESTAL

No matter how effective our interceptor defenses may be, we must always assume that a certain number of bombers will get through to the targets. We have no control over the choice of targets by an enemy but we can develop and allocate detector and interceptor defenses and we can reduce the attractiveness of our targets so that the expenditure of atomic bombs against them will be much less worthwhile. It is, then, a matter of prime importance to consider the attractiveness of the targets which we present to an enemy, to attempt to anticipate points of attack, and to study means for reducing the attractiveness. It is not necessary to have access to secret information to make reasonable estimates of target attractiveness. An analysis of easily obtained data permits a division into likely and unlikely targets. An exact priority list is not required.

TARGET ATTRACTIVENESS

The author is not a military man, skilled in selecting targets worth the time and effort involved in delivering atomic bombs on target. Furthermore, it is probable that the military attractiveness will change substantially during the course of time so that any specific target selections might be altered by later events. There are, however, some basic considerations which will undoubtedly be taken into account by any nation planning an attack upon us.

It is impossible to assess with certainty the value of our targets to an enemy whose decisions will be based on his particular war aims and colored by his psychological makeup but the following will undoubtedly rank high on his list of final choices:

1. Centers of population.
2. Industrial concentrations capable of producing items of military importance.
3. An individual plant producing a high percentage of an important war item.
4. Public utilities: electric power plants and water systems.
5. Transportation facilities into key areas.
6. Large dams and hydroelectric installations.
7. Military installations.

In many cases targets will be composites of the divisions listed and we must consider combinations in estimating the total target attractiveness. For example, industry and population tend to go together and the bomb may act against either element or both. At Hiroshima the death toll was large but the industrial areas, located largely on the outskirts of the city, were only slightly damaged and could have been restored to normal production in a short time had the war continued. At Nagasaki, on the other hand, the death toll was much smaller but severe damage was done to large manufacturing plants.

These differences were due to the arrangements of the two cities and not to any deliberate defense planning by the Japanese, but they serve to show how destruction can be altered by the layout of the target.

POPULATION AND INDUSTRY

The atomic bomb is a highly effective antipersonnel weapon and we would be negligent not to assume that it will be used against our centers of population, even those which do not contain key war industries. It is a moot point as to whether population bombing will ever play a major role in deciding a global war but it can certainly reduce the ability to retaliate promptly and hence it may be considered worthwhile by an aggressor.

The United States is an urban nation. Thirty percent of our population live in cities of 100 thousand or more, twelve percent are in cities of more than one million, and *one person in twenty lives in New York City.* At present some sixty percent of our population live in cities occupying less than three percent of the total land area and it appears that the urban concentration is increasing. Between 1940 and 1948 the population of the United States increased by more than 14 millions and more than 10 millions of the increase were in the urban communities. Many of these crowded cities are lush targets for an enemy interested in personnel bombing but this situation can be altered in the future by proper planning. Population densities and hence target attractiveness depend upon the desires of the people and how they want to live. If population densities can be reduced many of our cities will be more desirable and safer places in which to live.

Most of our cities have followed a familiar growth pattern. As the demands for industrial and living space increased, horizontal expansion would be limited by unfavorable transportation facilities or geography and vertical expansion was the usual result. This vertical expansion plays directly into the hands of the atomic bomber. Tall buildings increase the population density and bring more people within range of the penetrating radiations and the blast. Other things being equal, the more nearly a city is spherical or cubical the more destruction wrought by the bomb.

As a result of this vertical expansion population densities have risen and we now have as typical values:

New York City	21,000 per square mile
Chicago	16,000 " " "
Pittsburgh	12,000 " " "

These figures may be compared with those for essentially horizontal cities such as:

Los Angeles	3,000 per square mile
Houston	5,000 " " "

Obviously some of our cities are sitting ducks, well-fattened and inviting destruction. Cities like Los Angeles and Houston (Fig. 11-1, p. 115), which are not prize targets now, will become so if population densities are allowed to increase and if tall buildings are erected in compact clusters. Compactness is a poor exchange for immunity from attack. In the growing cities which are not now attractive to the atomic bomber, the choice is in the hands of the city planners, who will do well to weigh the facts before recommending new construction.

ATOMIC BOMB GEOGRAPHY

Not only have we concentrated large numbers of people into our cities but many of our larger and important cities are concentrated in a small portion of the nation. Our industrial might is primarily located in the Northeast and North Central regions, as can be readily seen from Fig. 11-2. In this industrial heart lie the trade and commerce of New York, the oil refineries of New Jersey, the rubber of Akron, and the Detroit automobile plants which were so important in producing the implements for World War II. Well over 80 percent of the nation's steel in-

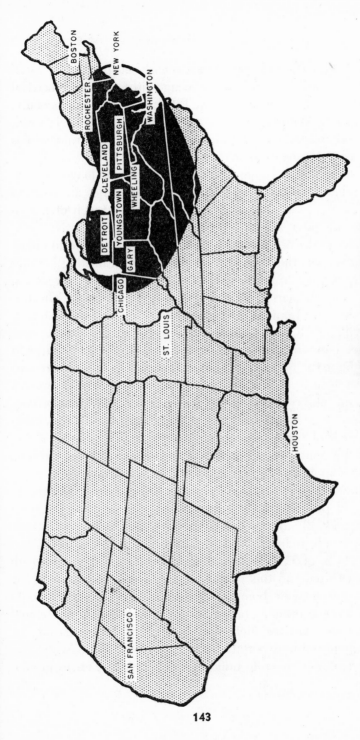

Fig. 11-2   The vulnerable heart of the United States.

dustry lies in the industrial heart—nearly 60 percent in Pittsburgh, Youngstown, and the Chicago area. Heavy electrical
machine construction centers at Pittsburgh and Schenectady,
chemicals at Wilmington; but the point need not be labored.
For good measure the nonindustrial seat of government lies
well within the heart area.

The heart area is vulnerable; the Alleghenys no longer present
a formidable natural barrier. Many of these cities are close to
the Atlantic coast and would be within easy reach of a sub-
marine-launched bomber. Many lie close to our Northern
boundary and this fact makes them more vulnerable to an attack from over the Pole. The more time an attacking bomber
must spend inside our borders before reaching its target the
better our chances for detection and interception. On this
basis alone St. Louis is a less desirable target than Cleveland;
Louisville less than Rochester.

True, many important industrial concentrations are scattered
throughout the nation but a severe bombing of the heart area
would seriously cripple the power of the country to wage a
war. Our ability to produce the tools of war in enormous
quantities has won the respect of all nations; an enemy would
consider it of the utmost importance to knock out this ability
before the initial inertia had been overcome and war production was in full swing. A bombing of the heart area would
probably not seriously damage our existing striking power and
we could probably institute retaliatory measures to the limit
of our stock piles but our potential for waging a long war might
be drastically reduced.

The bulk of East-West rail transportation funnels through
the heart area and this would be temporarily disrupted if the
area were heavily bombed. Transportation facilities would
scarcely be a primary target for an atomic bomb but would
suffer some damage incidental to that of the main targets.
Damage to rail transportation can be repaired more easily than
large steel and concrete buildings and the experiences in Ger-

many indicate that steadily maintained attacks are required to seriously disrupt rail traffic. When this can be accomplished, however, the effects on the ability to wage war are prompt and substantial.

CRITICAL FACILITIES

Outside the heart area are many special targets which are widely separated but of the greatest importance to us in waging a total war. The plants of the Atomic Energy Commission at Oak Ridge and Hanford are examples of facilities worthy of special attention by an aggressor. If these production plants were destroyed we would be forced to retaliate with less effective weapons after our initial stock pile of atomic weapons was exhausted.

Although these plants are vulnerable targets, as can be seen from Fig. 11–3 and 11–4 (pp. 116, 117), the enemy might plan to spare them in the hope that he might later exercise control over their output. However, if an aggressor felt that he could only gain his ends by a complete destruction of our warmaking facilities, these plants would certainly be among the first targets for attack.

The plants of the Atomic Energy Commission use substantial amounts of electric power and hence we must add to the list of critical facilities Norris Dam, Bonneville, Boulder, and Grand Coulee. Destruction of these dams would not affect the Atomic Energy Commission installations alone; the aluminum industry, for example, uses enormous quantities of electric power and most of this is obtained from hydroelectric plants. The difficulties of knocking out a dam became evident during the bombing of Germany but some of our dams are prizes worthy of a tremendous effort.

Another target of first order importance might be the lock system at Sault Ste. Marie, through which passes all of the iron ore from the famous Mesabi range. This is not an ordinary, easily repaired transportation facility. The closing of these locks would call for a superhuman effort to keep the furnaces of the heart area supplied and even in the atomic age steel remains the principal component of a war machine.

The examples cited are only samples of some of our special installations which would be particularly attractive to an atomic bomber. In many cases these highly valuable targets may be spared in the hope that through conquest they may be obtained intact but in our defense planning we can only assume that they will be targets of great attractiveness.

In general, top scientific personnel tend to concentrate around large installations which offer better opportunities for large-scale research. In some cases the loss of a few of our most important scientists would be far more serious than a large loss of plant. Whether we like it or not, it seems clear that scientists will implement future wars and hence they become among the most valuable of our assets for defense.

MILITARY INSTALLATIONS

Troops in the field and ships at sea will in general be so dispersed as to be scarcely worth an atomic bomb but some of the supporting installations may be highly desirable targets. One of these prizes is the Pentagon, Fig. 11-5 (p. 118). With the usual concentration of high brass housed here, the military services might be without high echelon leadership after a successful atomic attack. Atomic attacks on large naval bases such as those at Philadelphia, San Francisco, or Bremmerton would be severely damaging, both to the normal facilities and to any "mothball" fleets tied up there. These fleets represent the Navy in its most concentrated form—choice targets for atomic weapons. Again, Wright Field is a target whose destruction would seriously cripple the Air Force if it were forced to fight a long war.

With the present trend toward the use of more mechanized devices and the latest results of scientific research by all branches of the military it appears inevitable that large supporting bases will be required for any military operation of consequence. It would seem desirable to reduce the concentration of highly important facilities to a minimum consistent with efficient operation in order to reduce the target attractiveness.

POOR INVESTMENTS

Although the cost of manufacturing and delivering an atomic bomb on target is not known accurately, it is obvious that the bomb is not a bargain counter item and that the proper delivery will call for a specially planned and extensive operation. There are, then, targets for which the bomb is not to be considered. Small cities which do not contain a vital war industry are targets definitely unsuited for the power of the bomb. It is difficult to draw the line between the desirable and the undesirable but a good guess might be a population of 100,000. Of the select group some will be excluded because of a growth pattern unfavorable to destruction by one large bomb. Los Angeles for example might well escape atomic attack because its population and industries are spread rather thinly over a large area.

According to the 1940 census there are 92 cities in the good investment group and about one-half of these are in the heart area of Fig. 11–2. This then becomes the good investment area whereas the rest of the country is, on this basis, a relatively poor atomic target.

It is not our purpose to analyze specific cities in detail and attempt to separate probable from improbable targets. Those most competent to do this are the residents of the cities themselves. It behooves each thinking citizen to weigh the chances that his city will be on the preferred list of targets, any or all of which may be subjected to an atomic Pearl Harbor. Cities of borderline attractiveness should not dismiss the subject as one of no immediate concern, for the exact pattern of an enemy attack is seldom clear and some who least expect it may be deeply involved. It is indeed a problem for all citizens.

Chapter 12

DISASTER PLANNING

"It no longer is difficult to visualize an attack on American cities which would require earnest planning by serious-minded men and women with their nation's welfare and their own lives at stake—planning and organization which cannot wait for the attack to occur."

—Report by the Office of Civil Defense Planning

In addition to the purely military measures such as interception and antiaircraft fire, there are important defenses which involve the entire civilian population. One phase includes long-range planning for the dispersal of our large, compact units into smaller, less attractive targets. The second phase calls for planning for prompt directed action following the detonation of one or more atomic bombs. If the first phase is successfully carried out, we may reduce the attractiveness of our cities to a point where they are not worthy of an atomic bomb. They would still be targets for conventional weapons and sabotage, however, and hence disaster planning will be necessary even if decentralization is carried out on a large scale. Furthermore, we

148

can scarcely destroy our existing large cities and until obsolescence takes its toll these will remain prime targets whose last defense will be well-organized plans for disaster relief.

AN INTERIM SOLUTION

Although decentralization appears to offer the best long-range solution for reducing our vulnerability we must not assume that an enemy will obligingly withhold his attack until we have made that attack less attractive. Decentralization of our larger cities will be a long process and one which may never be as complete as we would like. It behooves us therefore to make immediate plans for combatting a devastating attack so that its effects may be kept at a minimum. The necessity for such planning does not arise from humanitarian motives alone—the fight for survival may require the utmost salvage of people and material from the wreckage following a surprise attack.

Hiroshima is an example of a lack of planning. With the local medical facilities almost completely destroyed, help was slow in coming and the general apathy and the inability of the local officials to organize relief was outstanding. No accurate figure can be given for the number of lives that could have been saved by prompt action but it would undoubtedly have been large. At Nagasaki shelters for many thousands were available but were scarcely used. An efficient detection system together with an enforced alert might have saved 80 percent of those who died.

With our system of communication and transportation and our experience in relief for peacetime disasters we should be able to do much better than did the Japanese. But can we at the present time adequately minister to the needs of ten of our larger cities simultaneously attacked with atomic bombs? In some ways we are little better off than the Japanese. They had heard nothing about the atomic bomb; we have been subjected to a barrage of publicity, but how little real practical information has reached the people!

Time may be running out and we can ill-afford to postpone longer our planning to minimize the effects of an attack that we hope will never come. Planning should start soon and should proceed rapidly but, above all, planning must be sound. We are a nation of doers, but we must not let doing precede planning. Our individualistic population must be made to realize that some regimentation and obedience to competent authority will be required if bad situations are not to be made worse. A large-scale undertaking of this nature is unique in our history but we must become accustomed to it. *Truly our days of peacetime indifference are numbered.* We may never again have an equal opportunity for preparation.

WHO SHOULD PLAN

In spite of the fact that a sound program is urgently needed, we must not fall into our common error of overactivity once we see what is to be done. Although we are using radioactive isotopes on a far larger scale than any other nation, we have never experienced a large-scale disaster in which radioactivity was involved and we have comparatively few men who have the training and experience for planning a comprehensive program. Much information is available but many questions can only be answered with educated guesses. The bulk of the casualties will in all probability be burns and blast injury cases and the treatment of these is well understood.

Although the technical background and the broad phases of the planning should originate from a central source, the details of the program are essentially a local matter. Each city will have needs and relief facilities peculiar unto itself and these can be best woven into the required pattern by the local authorities who are most familiar with them. The central agency must supply guidance and co-ordination but not compulsion and coercion.

Immediate planning need not be nationwide because many communities are marginal targets at best and tentative programs should first be worked out for the most vulnerable. The most sensitive area lies in the industrial heart and the cities located here are the most immediately concerned. All of this type of planning is new and it may be necessary to make changes during the development of the program. As the details smooth out, extensions of the program can be made to the marginal cities so that they will have supporting groups available should other areas be devastated.

THE PEACETIME VALUE

Any organization set up to cope with the aftermath of atomic attack will be of great value during peacetime as well. Disasters of nature and industry occur frequently and in spite of our good relief record there could be a decided improvement if well-trained relief organizations were available. Training of defense units will involve much more than an indoctrination into the hazards of radioactivity for, as we have seen, the atomic bomb brings fire and general destruction as well. Any disaster plan developed for atomic defense could be invoked at the time of a Texas City catastrophe, an earthquake, or a hurricane, and relief measures could be speeded by having competent direction of a large group of trained workers. Units of relief workers brought in from other areas would be able to work more effectively with the local organization if both had received training from a common source.

A well-designed program of training and indoctrination should do much to give the general public a more healthy attitude toward atomic warfare. The Atomic Age is here and we must accept the bad along with the good. As more information is released and interpreted for the layman the more he can see the hazards in their proper light. When the public realizes that useful relief organizations are being set up and that with properly trained medical personnel many lives can be saved, the present defeatist attitude toward the bomb may be replaced by the feeling that something can be done about it after all.

This would represent a considerable advance in morale and should substantially increase our ability to fight back after an attack.

THE MEDICAL CHALLENGE

The medical profession must assume the greatest responsibility for disaster relief. An immediate problem will be the enormous numbers of casualties who will be suffering from all sorts of injuries, those from burns and blast predominating. Some persons will appear to be uninjured but will have received sufficient radiation to be beyond medical help. Normal hospital facilities will be partially or totally destroyed and temporary structures must be utilized. To add to the difficulties, water, gas, and electric power may be cut off. Fires will spring up and may force the evacuation of front line aid stations.

In addition to the individual casualties, there will be serious public health problems. Inclement weather may require prompt housing of the survivors to avoid further deaths from exposure. Water supplies must be checked for radioactive contamination and arrangements must be made to restore distribution as soon as possible. Food supplies may be contaminated and must be checked before consumption. Sewage disposal will present a particularly important problem that must be dealt with promptly. Measures must be taken to prevent epidemics.

The rapid evacuation of casualties will be one of the most difficult problems. Local medical facilities will almost certainly be hard hit and many doctors will be incapacitated by the bomb. Adequate medical treatment will require that water and sewage systems remain in operation; a most unlikely situation. It seems inevitable that only emergency first aid can be administered on the scene, to be followed by prompt evacuation to hospitals, where adequate treatment can be obtained. Such an evacuation presents a tremendous problem in traffic control and transportation, particularly if other large cities nearby have suffered similar disasters.

There was a considerable delay in getting the victims of the Cocoanut Grove fire to hospitals because all streets were choked with traffic of the curious. When the streets were finally cleared, the victims were sent to only two hospitals, completely overtaxing their facilities, while other hospitals waited in vain for patients. The most careful planning and indoctrination will be required to prevent a repetition of this confusion on an enormous scale. Above all, public hysteria must be avoided and *the only weapon against hysteria is education.*

It may be necessary for the medical profession to adopt a new philosophy in the treatment of radiation casualties. Persons who have received lethal doses of radiation can scarcely be allowed to take up the time of the few doctors available, for we must assume that even with the best planning there will be a dearth of medical men and facilities during the first hours. Medical skill should be devoted to those marginal cases where there is at least some chance of success. This is not to suggest that measures for the relief of pain should be withheld, but only that there will not be time or facilities to permit last-ditch fights against overwhelming odds. The consequences of a large overdose of radiation, though delayed, are inevitable and barring future medical discoveries must be accepted as such. The question of deciding who has received a lethal dose will be an impossible one unless a personnel meter can be devised which is cheap enough to be supplied to everyone. It is not sufficient to estimate doses by calculation of the distance of the victim from the blast, as shielding will produce large local variations in dosage. Until such meters are developed, this discussion is of only philosophical interest.

In the present age of medical specialization there are many physicians who are not skilled in recognizing the symptoms of radiation sickness and who are not familiar with the latest developments in treatment. These men must be kept informed of the latest results of research and the preferred methods of treatment recommended by the leaders in the field. Fortunately, the basic training of physicians is sufficiently broad to permit them to be indoctrinated with a minimum of effort. The American Medical Association will do well to note the burden that may be thrust upon its members and to consider means for rendering all possible assistance. The various branches of the National Military Establishment have inaugurated a series of training courses which are providing a good nucleus of trained men. With proper integration, these various trained groups can be welded into a potent force for reducing the disaster toll.

THE SCOURGE OF FIRE

An intense firefighting effort will be most urgently needed immediately following an atomic bomb blast. Hundreds of fires may break out almost simultaneously and even with all facilities intact such a situation would present a serious problem to the most efficient fire department. With rubble-littered streets, water pressure gone, many men killed, and equipment ruined, the task will require superhuman effort. Firefighting equipment must be capable of moving through streets filled with the debris from shattered buildings, emergency sources of water must be available, equipment must be standardized so that help from other cities can be utilized, and planning must be thorough. Without all this, there is little use in studying maps neatly marked with areas of predicted damage—severe, moderate, minor. Fires originating in the damaged area can sweep unhindered over great areas untouched by the original blast.

Speed will be most essential if fires are to be kept from spreading and this will mean that firefighters may have to enter areas contaminated with radioactive fission products. It is probable that the contamination will not be of a high order and close coordination with the radiological survey parties will serve to evaluate the radiation hazards. For the common good, it may even be necessary to risk radiation sickness in a few.

A HOST OF PROBLEMS

The medical profession and the firefighters will bear the brunt of the defense measures but there are innumerable problems that will require the services of many skilled workers. Communications within the stricken area and to the outside world must be restored as soon as possible so that a complete picture of internal conditions will be constantly available to those directing the rescue efforts. Transportation facilities must be repaired rapidly so that casualties can be moved out and relief workers can get in. Rigid traffic controls must be established and maintained to prevent uninjured persons from entering dangerously contaminated areas. Strong law enforcement will be required to prevent looting and the responsibility for maintaining order must be clearly allocated. Plans for the overall administration of the area must be worked out in advance on the assumption that at least some of the local authorities will be lost in the attack.

Confusion and overlapping of authority and function must be avoided and this can be done only if there has been careful planning beforehand, with a thorough indoctrination of all key personnel in their individual responsibilities. Some temporization will inevitably be required but this must be kept to a minimum.

THE REAL PROBLEM

It is quite evident that each community represents a unique situation with distinct problems and for this reason it seems that the only feasible organization will be one in which the local authorities play a leading role. The local groups must fit into the general framework of the national system and all must speak the same technical language, but all details are purely local matters. The system must be better than that which produced the air raid wardens of World War II and considerable numbers of men and women must receive some training in the many phases of atomic disasters.

Municipal authorities should begin the formulation of their local problems but should not attempt independent solutions without technical guidance. The utmost confusion could result from a number of uncoordinated plans based on different bits of information, much of which may be out of date. We are playing for enormous stakes in lives and property and we can ill-afford to make mistakes. The task, though unpleasant, should not be regarded as an onerous burden forced on us by the evil intentions of foreign powers. Rather, it should be considered as a challenge to our democratic way of life and as an opportunity to show that we are able to cope with any situation. The challenge is a personal one and the way in which it will be answered depends on each one of us as an individual.

Chapter 13

DISPERSION

"I believe we have finally learned that national defense is not the exclusive property and concern of men in uniform, but the responsibility as well of labor, management, agriculture, industry, and every group that goes to make up the national complex."
—GEN. D. D. EISENHOWER

Indirectly, the atomic bomb offers a rare opportunity for greatly improving the living conditions of millions of our citizens. Our large cities have been growing larger, resulting in more crowded streets and tenement houses. Now that the bomb is here and we are not *certain* that we can live in peace with our global neighbors, we must start at once to reduce our target attractiveness by dispersion and if this is done properly we will at the same time greatly increase our urban attractiveness. The bomb is forcing a social revolution comparable in scope to the industrial revolution brought about by the introduction of steam and electric power. The same technology that developed the bomb should be able to solve the problems of this social revolution and lead the nation to a better and a safer way of life.

GOING DOWN?

It has been stated that in the atomic age the only safe locations are in deep underground caverns where we must live, work, and prepare retaliatory efforts against our enemies. There is no doubt that deep underground shelters provide the ultimate protection against the atomic weapons we know today. Many feet of earth will reduce even tremendous neutron and gamma ray intensities to safe values. With a sufficient thickness of overlying earth the impact of the blast wave will be absorbed and the buried chambers will be left unharmed.

It is not practicable to obtain comparable shielding through the construction of above-ground structures with thick walls of concrete or other materials. The usual masonry construction will afford some measure of protection but absolute safety can be obtained only in deep natural caves or in deep excavations. Must we, then, resign ourselves to a mole-like existence as the only alternative to a life of constant fear? The answer is emphatically, "No."

Certainly, stock piles of materials absolutely vital to the national security might well be located in underground shelters for the greatest possible protection. It is quite possible that certain highly specialized activities, perhaps plants producing materials of the greatest importance to the national defense, may be advantageously located underground. The number of such plants would be small and their activities such that underground operation would be feasible without extraordinary effort for maintenance. For example, the assembly of some vital part of a complex instrument might well be carried on underground. On the other hand, it is doubtful that any plant operating large furnaces could be successfully located underground because of the tremendous amount of fresh air required.

The number of satisfactory natural caves is small, few if

any abandoned mines can be used, and the cost of deep-large-scale excavation is high. Any attempt to put the bulk of our manufacturing facilities underground would be so prohibitively expensive that it is doubtful that our economy could stand the strain, even if the cost were spread over many years. Similarly, large-scale housing projects could scarcely be buried at a reasonable cost.

The psychological effects of going underground would be at least as serious as the economic disruption. A nation changing its mode of living in so drastic a manner would be almost certain to acquire a defeatist attitude that would reduce the effectiveness of any countermeasures directed against an aggressor. In the past the people of the United States have lived without fear of large-scale destruction and they must continue to do so. To seek shelter as a nation would be to admit a helplessness not at all in accord with the facts.

DISPERSION IS LIFE INSURANCE

Although a mass movement into underground shelters seems unwise and impractical, there is no reason to neglect less drastic measures that would reduce the attractiveness of our targets and yield a minimum return to the atomic bomber. One of the most attractive measures that can be undertaken is the dispersal of our large centers of population and our industrial concentrations over large areas. It is difficult to conceive of any military weapon that would be more effective against a less concentrated target and a horizontal dispersion would be an effective method of reducing the devastation produced by any weapon. *Like life insurance, dispersion is protection against a disaster we hope will never come.*

In recommending dispersion we do not advise the immediate evacuation of our large cities, with a subsequent rebuilding in less concentrated form. Such a drastic removal would have economic and psychological consequences comparable to those of a mass underground movement. At present we have

our large cities and we are stuck with them. Given the right
impetus a decentralization movement might start spontane-
ously and gradually reduce the population and industrial concentrations so that in 10 or 20 years there would be fewer lush
targets for attack.

Buildings and factories become obsolete or unsafe for occu-
pancy and must be torn down or replaced. In most urban areas
the tendency in the past has been to replace with a taller structure in order to gain more space from a given area of land.
If some obsolete structures were torn down and not replaced
and if the activities were relocated in accordance with some
reasonable plan, a gradual decentralization would result. Isolated skyscrapers do not warrant the expenditure of an atomic
bomb but concentrations of large buildings make ideal targets.

To be successful, dispersion must be according to plan but
must not be ordered or directed. Individuals must be made to
see the desirability of such moves and must choose new locations with guidance but without pressure. It does not appear
feasible to work out a national master plan for decentralization.
Local geography and the particular requirements of the individual industries must govern the actual details. Broad principles applicable to all communities can be laid down but each
city will have problems peculiar unto itself.

In any dispersion plan adequate transportation is of para-
mount importance. Rail and highway facilities must be carefully planned in advance so that adequate service is available
during peacetime and interruptions are at a minimum if the
area comes under attack. Perhaps new, radically different modes
of transportation may be developed to meet the needs of decentralization. While communications have advanced from the
telegraph to television the chief advances in railroading have
been the development of the air brake and the substitution of
Diesel engines for wood-burners.

NO MASS EXODUS

Any program for dispersion is necessarily a long-range plan looking for results in 10 or 20 years. We can not abandon our cities or scatter our centralized industries overnight without seriously disrupting our economy and our way of life. Our vulnerable targets will remain so for some time but with a good dispersion program the attractiveness will become less and less until many pass from the attractive class to the poor investment. Industry and the population at large must be made to see the collateral advantages of decentralization so that they will take the initiative, under guidance, that will eventually lead not only to a reduced target attractiveness but also to a better way of living.

The "noble experiment" of national prohibition showed that the people of the United States can not be coerced or legislated into doing something in which they do not believe. They will react vigorously against any attempt to force decentralization and any premature or ill-considered program will probably meet sufficient resistance to render it useless. The facts must be presented to the people in an honest, unemotional manner free from hysteria but with no attempt to minimize the gravity of the situation. Widespread education is the force needed to start the movement which, after a time, should proceed under its own momentum.

An adequate program need not go to the extreme of uniformly spreading all people and industry over all of the acceptable land in the nation. This would reduce the attractiveness well below that needed to discourage the use of the bomb but would introduce insoluble problems of transportation and would withdraw land needed for agriculture and forests. Rather, the plan should contemplate the spreading out of industry and residences into closely knit but not highly concentrated units. These units might consist of a series of small satellite cities with the individual units separated by perhaps 3

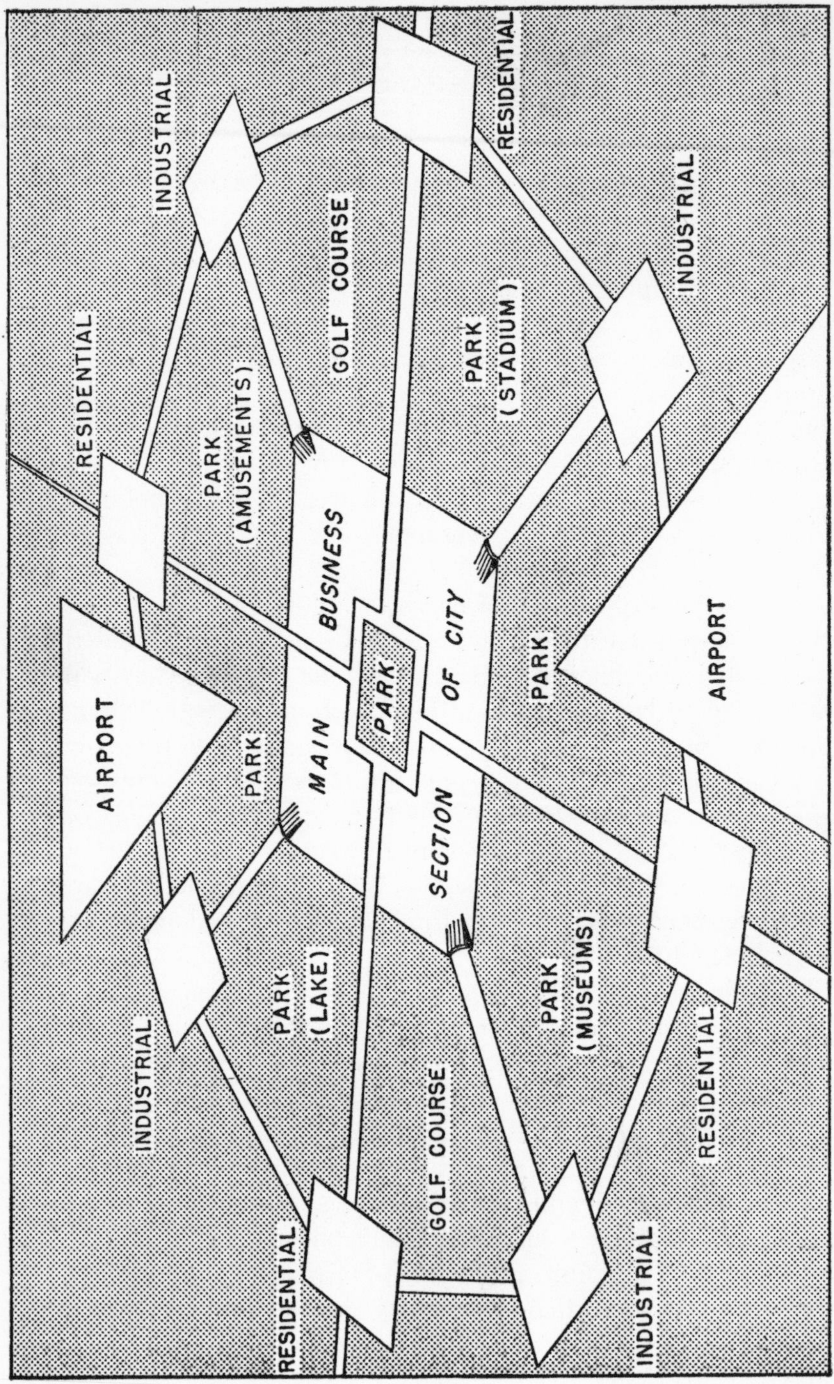

Fig. 18-1. The satellite city.

The labels in the figure include: INDUSTRIAL, RESIDENTIAL, GOLF COURSE, PARK (AMUSEMENTS), PARK (STADIUM), PARK, MAIN BUSINESS SECTION OF CITY, AIRPORT, INDUSTRIAL, PARK (LAKE), GOLF COURSE, PARK (MUSEUMS), RESIDENTIAL, INDUSTRIAL

162

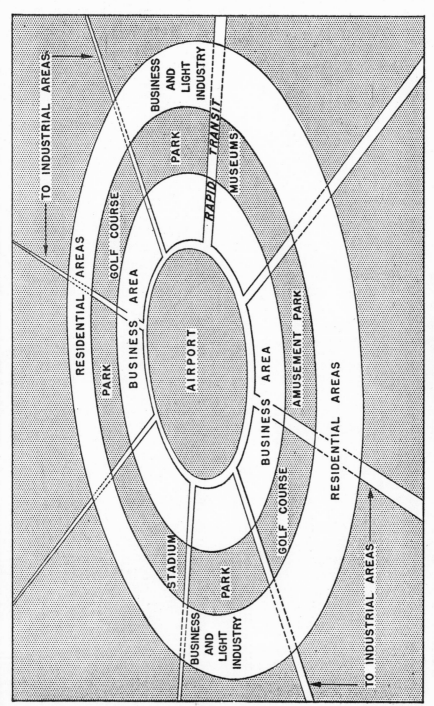

Fig. 13-2 The doughnut city.

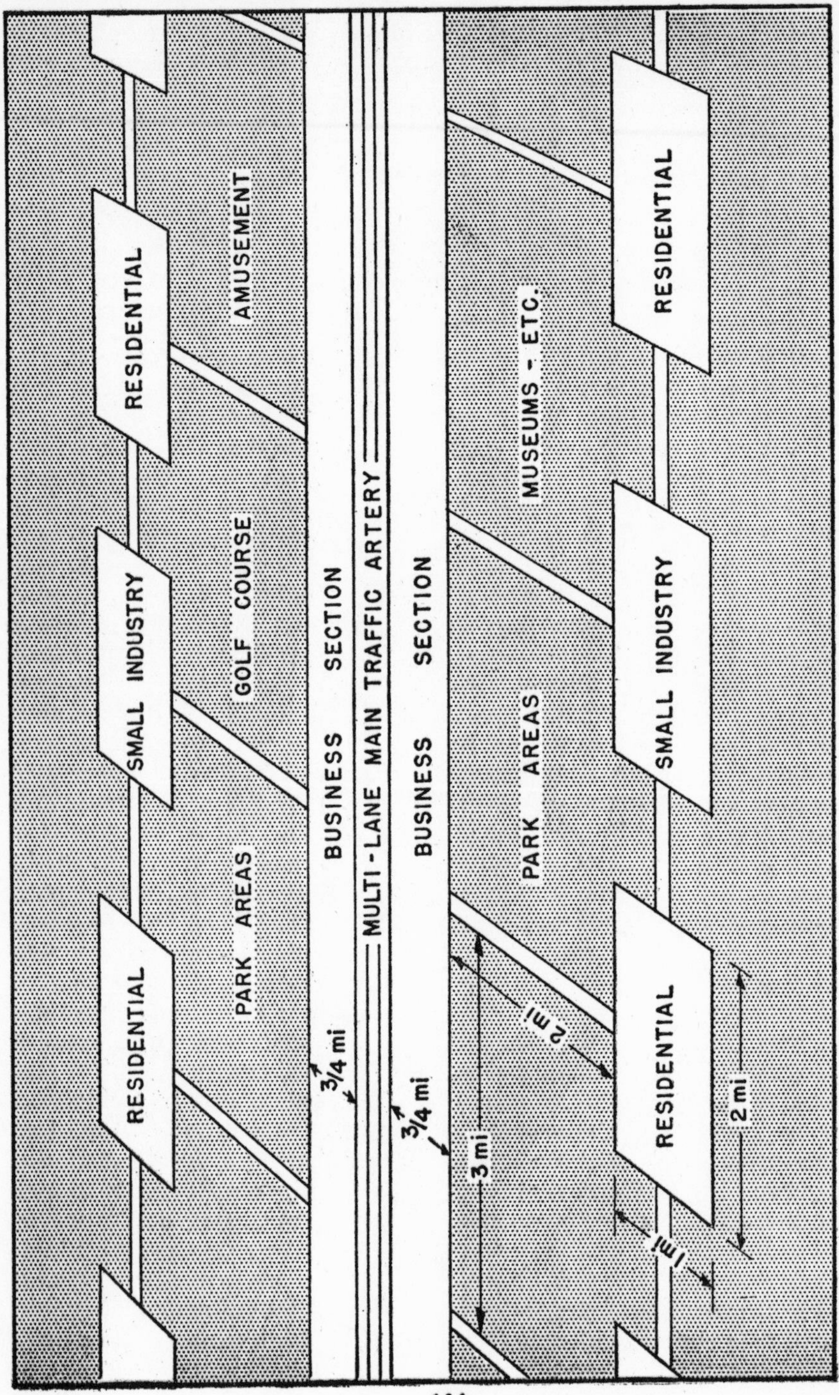

Fig. 12.3. The rodlike city

miles, as shown in Fig. 13–1. Another possibility is the dough-nut city, Fig. 13–2, in which the usual congested central area is replaced by a park or airport, with the important facilities located around the periphery. The rod-like city, Fig. 13–3, might make for a simple solution of the transportation problem if the geography permitted such a development.

These are only suggestions as to the way in which decentralization should go. Other satisfactory arrangements can undoubtedly be worked out but in any plan care should be taken to keep a minimum distance of about 3 miles between the components of the development. The location of relief facilities such as hospitals and fire stations should receive special attention.

THE OPTIMUM CITY

A good decentralization program would not only reduce the target attractiveness but would also improve the living conditions for many people now crowded into our larger cities. Many people could exchange an environment of concrete and canyonlike streets for green grass and sunlight. Automobile parking, an acute problem in practically every city, could be more adequate in a properly decentralized development. The per capita numbers of suicides and most major crimes are definitely higher in urban communities and the effect of crowded living conditions on juvenile delinquency is well known. With proper decentralization these antisocial manifestations should show a decrease. Decentralization would not produce a Utopia but it would certainly result in a better rather than a worse environment.

It is probable that there is a certain size of city which operates with the greatest efficiency. In smaller cities some of the facilities of the larger units cannot be operated with profit. In the larger cities sheer bulk makes for traffic congestion. The exact size of the most efficient city is difficult to determine but there is evidence that it is not far from 100,000. This is just about the marginal size which, barring special considerations, makes a city a possible target for an atom bomb. If the units in a decentralized development were kept under this figure each would be a rather poor investment for the atomic bomber yet each would be a relatively self-sufficient entity.

In planning decentralization careful consideration must be given to the location of certain critical facilities. Much of the horror of Nagasaki was caused by the almost complete destruction of the hospitals. Obviously, any new medical construction should be located with due consideration of its proximity to attractive bomb targets. This should be true even if a comprehensive decentralization plan is not in operation. Hospitals, public utilities, fire and police stations are examples of facilities that should be located only after carefully considering the possible damage from an attack.

In spite of the fact that the recent population increases have been predominantly in the urban areas there are some indications of a trend toward decentralization. Steel facilities have been opened up on the west coast and some plants are locating on the outskirts of cities rather than seeking sites near the centers. Some industries have found that manufacturing costs are lower in smaller communities and are leading the way to adequate dispersal. There is a slight movement of city dwellers toward suburban housing but many of these developments are in the higher price brackets, and in many cases public transportation is inadequate. These slight trends suggest that decentralization is not an idealist's dream but a practical solution to several of our national problems, and with a little encouragement the trends might become movements of sufficient magnitude to produce significant results.

Encouragement and guidance is already available. The National Security Resources Board created by the National Security Act of 1947 is charged with "the strategic relocation of industries, services, government, and economic activities, the continuous operation of which is essential to the Nation's security." The Board has made careful studies of the problems of relocation and is vigorously proceeding to undertake the initial phases of this work.

THE COST

When the national security is involved, cost is not a primary consideration but it will be well to consider the possible costs of a significant decentralization program. To be practical, it appears that for the most part the program would have to be self-supporting. The owner of a business or factory will have to be shown that he can operate with equal or greater efficiency under the new arrangement and that it may well be to his advantage to transfer his activities to a less vulnerable location. This again calls for an intensive program of education which must be based on cold facts and figures and not on idealistic thinking. Perhaps some industries cannot advantageously move into a decentralized area. Should there be some form of national subsidy which would enable them to move or should they be left to take their chances against attack? A national subsidy appears to be unwise for many reasons. Rather it would seem desirable to seek industries which *can* move advantageously and thus reduce the concentration. We repeat, *to be successful dispersion must be planned but voluntary, not haphazard or forced.*

It is true that some encouragement and support may be needed to start the ball rolling. This is particularly true of public utilities and transportation systems. These are prerequisites for any horizontal expansion and we can scarcely expect them to be built with private capital long before the demand exists nor can we expect expansion long before the supporting facilities are available. It would seem, therefore, that such expenditures would be a justifiable public expense.

The total investment will be large but it need not all be an added burden to the taxpayer. At the present time the budget for national defense is about 15 billion dollars. Surely a sound decentralization program is a national defense measure and as such might be partially financed from defense appropriations. Jet interceptors to repel bombers are a legitimate defense expenditure, and money spent to reduce the chance of being bombed seems equally justified.

Decentralization is a long-range movement which will not be accomplished or paid for in a few years. If a billion dollars a year were spent for 10 or 20 years, it would go a long way towards catalyzing the spontaneous movement without which decentralization cannot succeed in a democracy. If it succeeds we will have a better and safer nation with none of the adverse psychological reactions that would certainly accompany a mass underground movement.

Chapter 14
OF THE FUTURE

"When the time is run, and that future has become history, it will be clear how little of it we today foresaw or could foresee."

— J. ROBERT OPPENHEIMER

Today we are neither at peace nor at war. Our current state has been widely described as a "cold" war to distinguish it from a "shooting" war. Moreover, this same state of tension may continue for many years. General Omar Bradley has said "While this tension is disagreeable to those who clamor for peace, it is vastly preferable to war." Meanwhile the specter of war looms on the horizon and, in spite of all plans to the contrary, an incident might develop which would set off an irrevocable chain of events ending in armed conflict. Discounting this possibility, however, it seems from our line of reasoning that a war between two world powers will probably not take place before 1960.

The nations of the world are only just beginning to struggle to their feet from the effects of the last war. Many cities in Europe are still in ruins. All that has been done to date is to clean up the debris and arrange the chaos in orderly piles. Reconstruction is still in its early stages. And in this country, the United States is looking to its defenses.

FOR THE DEFENSE

No longer is national security measured in terms of home defense or in terms of purely military measures. Farseeing leaders have clearly recognized that *international order and national security are synonymous.* To this end, the nation's statesmen have persisted in an attempt to use the United Nations as the instrument for world peace. To the same end, our country is sponsoring the costly Marshall Plan to revive a weakened Europe to meet the threat of westward aggression and our leaders, with the consent of the people, have determined upon a plan of military preparedness. Preparedness is a very broad term. It was most wisely defined by General Eisenhower in his Final Report as Chief of Staff as "a state of organized readiness to meet external aggression by a timely mobilization of public opinion, trained men, proved weapons, and essential industries, together with the unmatched spiritual resources of America, all integrated into the most effective instrument of armed defense and reinforced by the support of every citizen in the form and measure necessary to the preservation of our way of life."

There has recently been much public discussion about the relative roles which the Army, Navy, and newly created Air Force will play in the rearmament program. Congress voted for the establishment of a 70-Group Air Force and it is the custom of the Congress, as the elected instrument of the people, to scrutinize the expenditures of the Military Establishment and to allot specific yearly appropriations to each Service. The people thus determine the kind of military machine that will be built. For example, they determine the number of troops in the Army; this they do directly or by exercising control over the funds allotted to the Ground Forces. In discussion of such a topic as the size of the Air Force, the principal issues have not always been clearly defined. Just what is the function of the 70-Group Force? Is it to provide a single striking force capable of obliterating the enemy from the air? . . . Is it to be our chief reliance in a future war? . . . or what is the mission of this huge force? At this point we should like to emphasize again a simple truth, the importance of which cannot be overstated: *A powerful strategic air force armed with atomic bombs may deliver a serious blow to enemy production facilities and man-power resources, but it is less capable of striking at the force-in-being of enemy bombers and A-bombs which have been ac-cumulated prior to the outbreak of hostilities.* It will be of small consolation to the atom-bombed people of Philadelphia to learn that our strategic air force has obliterated Moscow. Or imagine how frustrated air power could be if Russia pushed through Germany, overran the Low Countries, and took France. Would atomic bombs stop such a push? This would be tantamount to asking if the A-bomb could be used as an effective tactical weapon against land armies.

We can not afford to hide from such questions. Hiding will not help. The history book shows us that war follows age-old patterns. In fact, someone has said that "the more war changes, the more it remains the same." Such might well apply to a future war in Europe. It will be well for Americans to stop thinking that atomic bombs and high-speed bombers are all that we need. How, for example, would these prevent a west-ward push from the Baltic to the English Channel? Would even a very large number of A-bombs prove an effective deterrent to such a push? The author's personal belief is that it would not.

ENOUGH A-BOMBS?

Our atomic armament program, now costing close to a bil-lion dollars a year, is not subject to public scrutiny. As tax-payers, we appropriate much money per year, but we are told nothing about the numbers of atomic bombs produced. This is done in the name of security. The average citizen does not know whether we have 10, 100, 1,000, or 10,000 bombs. While the exact figure is TOP SECRET and we would not advocate disclosure at this time, it seems to us that the people of this country need to know *something more than nothing*. We believe that this information is necessary if the average American is to make wise decisions in the future. He must have facts to make decisions. The magnitude of our A-bomb stock pile ties in directly with the way in which the bombs may be used in future military operations. Are we going to depend upon the A-bombs alone and, if so, will they be used indiscriminately? There is no doubt that the A-bomb is an *effective* weapon but it is not a *decisive* weapon. *It will be tragic for Americans to discover this truth too late.*

To orient the thinking of the average person with regard to numbers of A-bombs which may be available at some time in the future, we note from Dr. Oppenheimer's testimony before a U. S. Senate Committee that it would be possible to accumulate 1,000 bombs within two years provided an all-out effort were made. If our atomic stock pile is to be measured in such terms, just where will we count our security? Will we at any given time increase our security by doubling the stock pile? An answer to such a question merely raises another, namely, when will we have *enough* atomic bombs? Enough for what? Obviously, enough to win a war. But herein lies the rub. The phrase "win a war" needs redefinition in modern times. Behind the apparent simplicity of these words lies the fundamental problem which confronts the military planners. Traditionally, military men have been assigned the task of implementing a war effort. Today the nation must prepare for the eventuality of winning a war in such a way as to win the peace as well.

NATIONAL WAR AIMS

Prior to the outbreak of hostilities, we must determine this nation's war aim. In the last war the principle of *unconditional* surrender was established. In the light of our past experience, this policy, as extended to Japan, seems inadequate and short-sighted. It did not win the peace and it probably lengthened the war. We must not again make similar mistakes. Our thinking must go beyond the cessation of battle and embrace the aftermath of war.

For example, if we were to press for unconditional surrender in a war with Russia, it would probably be accomplished only by physical invasion of Russian home soil. Most military men shudder at this prospect. Years of effort would be required to mount such an invasion and the cost would be staggering. Perhaps the reader is thinking, "Could not an initial air blitz of Russia succeed in breaking the will of the people to resist?" *Herein lies the great unknown.* Some think it could, some think it impossible. No one really knows. This line of thought is not pursued further here because it seems apparent that as a nation we should adopt a somewhat new concept of a war aim. If war can not be prevented, it may at least be *limited*. The concept of a limited war may seem incongruous, but it really is not. Rather than strive for complete subjugation of an enemy, his force-in-being should be neutralized. That is, his strategic bombers should be eliminated and insofar as possible territorial aggression should be stemmed. *Our striking force should seek to prevent the enemy from launching an air attack by concentrating as much as possible upon his means of delivery.*

We should subscribe to the authority of a United Nations organization before which international disputes could be brought even in time of war. In order to "bring the case into court" every conceivable pressure should be brought to bear on the aggressor. In the long run it would seem inadvisable to apply pressure purely by means of violence exerted against centers of population. As an alternative, we could rely upon psychological warfare, in which we would use ideas as weapons. This depends partially, of course, upon the concept that people themselves do not want war and would be susceptible to rational approaches, especially if they saw evidence of the ability of the enemy to deliver atomic bombs against them. In a sense, this is bringing war to the people.

In any such campaign, it is obvious that air power must play a decisive role but perhaps in a different character than presently anticipated. Since war is to be brought home to the people, it is clear that psychological and social forces may be more important than purely military weapons. One recalls, for instance, how amazed Russian soldiers were to discover that privates in the American Army wore wrist watches. Communist teachings were given a severe jolt by these minor incidents. Many such subtle approaches can be followed and more would evolve from serious thinking on the subject. The employment of psychological warfare is attractive if for no other reason than that it is a cheap weapon which does not require critical materials or much manpower.

We believe that the concept of a limited war is no more paradoxical than that of a strike of a labor group against an employer. Both sides know that a strike is mutually harmful, but strikes are still held to force the situation to a decision, often at the direction of a third neutral party. In the case of international disputes, a third disinterested party is less of a reality but once a tribunal composed of fair-minded men deals objectively with a dispute and renders sound decisions, faith will be built up in it. Furthermore, when this tribunal is backed up by the strong hand of a United Nations police force, decisions will be easier to enforce. This happy situation does not now prevail and the only course presently feasible for the United States is to insure its security through a program of preparedness.

A PREVENTIVE WAR?

In the streets of America talk is heard of a *preventive* war. There are some who argue that we should attack while we still have A-bomb supremacy. Why wait, they ask, until others have the bomb? More than a few are wondering if this is not the only way out. This is not necessarily a reflection upon the judgment of the American people; it is a natural consequence of our present paradox of "arming for peace" and at the same time "getting tough." Some persons have over-reacted to this program and without thinking the problem through have arrived at the concept of a preventive war. What is it that we are seeking to prevent? In a few words, we are seeking to repel Communism from Western Europe and other localities where it is an unwanted ideology. How then could this spread of the Red Doctrine be prevented by a war? We must realize that communistic influence extends into many lands. In the Orient, the Red-inspired offensive has pushed to the shores of the Pacific. In Europe it is meeting more resistance but even this might be overcome in time of crisis . . . if Russia, for example, sensed a preventive war in the offing. Could we then use the A-bomb on a Western Europe overrun by the Communists? The answer, obviously, is "no."

Atomic bombs do not guarantee victory but if we were "lucky" in a preventive war and "won," how would we deal with the conquered country? Remember that vanquished people do not feel kindly disposed toward the conqueror, especially in a war where atomic bombs are used. Such a war would settle nothing. In the process we might even lose that which we cherish most—our democratic form of government. A preventive war might well be long drawn out and very destructive. Remembering the burden imposed by the task of rebuilding a shattered Europe, how much greater would be the effort needed to reconstruct an atomic-bombed continent! Here we might easily see the renascence of Communism in the chaos of the postwar period. We might have won a war only to have the vanquished rise again in the form of new converts to this single-purposed ideology.

We are witnessing today a clash of ideologies. Our own must become stronger with time even in the face of Communism. At the same time, we must make ourselves militarily strong to resist physical aggression. Our shell of armor must not become too heavy or it may make inroads upon our national economy and result in inflation. Such conditions leave the back door wide open to infection from the Communist plague. Top planners in government circles realize this risk and appreciate that an extensive rearmament program can be a double-edged weapon. As we arm our nation with the instruments of war, we must also look to our internal armament—the provision of the American people with the means to reinforce the strength of our democratic society.

THE COST OF WAR

If for no other reason than that full-scale wars are too expensive, we should give some thought to a limited war. Not that even a limited war will not be expensive, but it may not involve all the kinds of expense which are paid in an all-out war. In the days of George Washington it cost about 2 million dollars per month of battle, whereas the last war ran up to the huge sum of almost 20 billions per month. The dollar value we have used for World War II is the total that we have estimated on the basis of projected payments for veterans and interest on the national debt. The latter two costs usually equal or surpass the actual direct costs of war.

War costs more than dollars and cents. It steals away from a nation the finest of its youth and this is a cost which defies monetary evaluation. It leaves behind scars of mental anguish. Many return from war broken in body and spirit. In addition to depriving our nation of men, there is the overwhelming drain on our natural resources; our oil, iron ore, critical minerals, and scarce metals. These are things with which nature has been bountiful in some cases, and niggardly in others. Our oil reserves continue to decline, our high-grade iron ores are being depleted. Another war like the one just past will see the American people deprived of more than merely their Sunday driving. War will become increasingly expensive even in the age of atomic weapons. *The atom bomb has not made war cheap.*

But more than the things we lose through war, we must count the things *we do not gain.* For the fiscal year 1950, President Truman asked for a total budget of 42 billion dollars. Out of this, 31 billions were for wars, past and future. Of every tax dollar, 74 cents are spent for military preparedness, aid to Europe, payment on the debt, or for veterans' relief. Just think of the public works program we could enjoy, the schools we could build, and the model communities that could be developed if we could spend these billions constructively! Today these are idle thoughts except for the concept of dispersion of our cities and factories. A few billion spent each year on decreasing the vulnerability of our nation to atomic attack will be of lasting value. Similarly, money spent for the Marshall Plan will have lasting effect.

Modern war is the most expensive business on earth. In spite of the fact that man invents new weapons of mass destruction which grow continually more devastating, warfare continues to rise in cost. In the case of high explosive bombs, for example, *a 1-ton bomb* in the last war cost a little over one hundred dollars and *killed an average of two people when used in Europe.* However, the "delivery costs" far surpassed the cost of the materials and ran the *cost per person killed to several thousand dollars.* One might wryly comment "Who said a person's life is cheap?" One might think that the development of the atomic bomb would reverse the trend in costs of war, but a look at the annual budget of the Atomic Energy Commission shows that this is not true. Furthermore, the huge B–36s needed for long-range bombing will probably cost two million dollars each when available in production quantities. There is, however, one bit of consolation for the taxpayer. Atomic bombs, unlike the aircraft that may deliver them, do not obsolesce. They have the unique characteristic of being redeemable for peacetime application in atomic power plants. *For the first time in the history*

*of military weapons, we can stockpile a critical item of equip-
ment and regard it as "money in the bank."*

NATIONAL DEFENSE

In spite of the fact that A-bombs, planes, and the other
hardware of war are expensive, we can not afford to be without
them during the present critical period. Since we are spending
so much for security, it is only reasonable to assure ourselves
that this money and effort buy the best and most effective
national defense.

Only recently has the traditional setup of the Armed Forces
been changed from a War and Navy Department team to a
single office of National Defense and three Departments—the
Army, Navy, and Air Force. In view of the awesome proportions of a future war, it would seem that the best interests of
national security would be served by a single defense organization. The Army, Navy, and Air Force must be welded into the
same type of land-sea-air efficiency as the Navy illustrated in
World War II with its force of submarines, surface and aviation units, and Marines. In the process, we must always be fear-
ful of the risk run by having a single Service dominate completely. Military groups, particularly in peacetime, when their
authority is not challenged by an enemy, tend to do their best
to prove right the saying of Lord Acton, "Power corrupts.
Absolute power corrupts absolutely." Healthy competition and
searching argument eliminate the corruption which one-party
systems invite. The problems of atomic warfare present truly
challenging problems to military men and they can not be attacked in either an Army, a Navy, or an Air Force approach;
rather, they must be approached with the single concept of
national security in mind. Anything less would result in a
World War II approach to the problem; in its execution alone,
this would wreck our national economy. What are required are
new approaches, breaks with the past, radical techniques, and
a great deal of original thinking to make the weaponry and

techniques of war simpler than at present. Thinking must be done by men who know no devotion to a single Service except that of their country. This country is fortunate in numbering among its military officialdom many fine young officers who think beyond the problems of the day. It is imperative that they be encouraged to continue their efforts in this direction and that they be supplemented by a fresh supply of officers attracted from civilian life.

In the same way, we must be sure that this nation maintains its present leadership in technical research and development. The last war showed conclusively that a country such as Germany could continue the development of new tools of war even under duress. Many surprising technical developments came from German laboratories; some surpassed our own and were often more than a mere embarrassment to our fighting men. *We might still be fighting in Germany if her scientists had had more time.* We cannot assure ourselves of the best in weapon development merely by appropriating more dollars for it. This, in fact, may even impede progress in certain lines. In a way, the atomic bomb development was very unfortunate, for it led many to believe that if you want something, no matter how fantastic, all you have to do is lay the money on the line and the problem will be solved. Too few realize that research is measured in terms of the ability of the men who spearhead it. A few men mean the difference between a vigorous productive laboratory and one which grinds out insignificance. Hundreds of technicians and rooms full of gleaming apparatus all go for naught if the inspiration, imagination, and creativeness of excellent research men are lacking. Even if these are present, the laboratory can become a house of frustration if there is not present on the administrative side a willingness to back new ventures and to accept the possibility of failure. A laboratory that has no failures is a really unique research institution.

No man knows what new instruments of war will be evolved from the research of today and one is tempted to think that we have almost approached a maximum in our ability to inflict destruction. If so, we must be quick to realize the significance of new weapons of war which may be contributed by the sociologist and others who deal in things besides physical science.

National defense must not be considered solely as a military matter. *National defense is a personal problem.* Moral force must also serve. As Winston Churchill put it, this force "is, unhappily, no substitute for armed force but it is a very great reinforcement." We are living in a dangerous age in days marked by the foreboding of sharp disaster. In such times, we can not solve the problem of national security by merely appropriating more billions for defense. Security is not bought that easily. We must be prepared to work hard for our future freedom and to do so we must match our force of arms with force of ideas. Clearly, we must show that our form of government, which glorifies the dignity of man, is superior to any other. Here our thinking must not be *defensive;* rather we should seize the initiative and use it to advantage.

A NOTE OF OPTIMISM

Optimism does not come easily in the present days of the Atomic Age. There are forces at work, however, which do not direct toward pessimism. That we do not see a way out of our present impasse does not mean that none exists. As Oppenheimer has so sagely commented: "It is in our hands to see that the hope of the future is not lost because we were too sure we knew the answers, too sure that there was no hope."

Just as the selfsame technology that led to the development of large cities now makes possible the dispersion of metropolitan areas into healthier communities, so may modern technology override the menace of the A-bomb. With better means of communication, each portion of the world community will better understand the problems and viewpoints of the others. Television will bring the world to the home of the average man. Modern medicine will triumph over diseases which have plagued heretofore uninhabitable land masses. Advances in agriculture will open still others to cultivation and permit support of new world communities. Education will achieve new standards of dissemination and coverage. Eventually, we may expect that atomic technology will provide a relatively cheap source of power, independent of the resources of the area it serves. Such a development would constitute a remarkable milestone in world affairs, for war in the past has often been a manifestation of the struggle for natural sources of energy. Witness how today world attention focuses on the rich oil fields of the Middle East.

As a nation, we are perpetually in a hurry. We seem to be always in a rush, hurrying after a street car—often not even looking to see where it is bound. We like to do big things and we want to do them quickly. Peace is the biggest thing in the world today and at this we must not fail. But we must not despair if our initial efforts seem in vain or meet with constant rebuff. History is replete with instances where there seemed no way out of a terrible impasse. It is illuminating and somewhat consoling to see in the writings of Richelieu, Cromwell, and many others that things were also black in the past. World accord will not be achieved overnight and, fortunately, there are yet some years of grace for further deliberation.

In our fight for freedom we are not alone. The dynamic effect of the Marshall Plan is to counteract the venom of Communism in Europe. Other democracies join in the fight against the Red menace. Nor is our only instrument that of force. There is a new awakening of spirit within the democracies. No longer is the problem of national security viewed solely as that of one nation. The security of a country and of the world are one and the same. It has taken the harsh implication of the atomic bomb to bring realization of this truth.

Force and freedom seem strange bedfellows. Can we live in a world with both? By far the best answer was given by James B. Conant when he wrote:

"If all concerned keep in the forefront of their minds the vital issue, the survival of our free society, then we may believe the eventual decisions will be sound. We must never falter in our faith in the moral basis of this republic. On these terms and these alone can we hope to resolve the paradox of force and freedom in the atomic age."

Throughout this book we have not attempted to draw too many conclusions. Rather, we have tried to present the facts as we know them. We believe that Americans can be trusted to arrive at the right conclusions when they are armed with facts. Once the average citizen knows and understands the truth, he will become the guiding beacon by which this nation sets its course. The nations of the world, surveying the uncharted waters ahead, look to this democracy for inspiration and hope. We have confidence that our democratic society will not falter; *it will survive.* The real issues are not cloaked in secrecy but are squarely before us. We have a responsibility from which *we must not hide.*